THE BET

People always seem to be busy nowadays, sometimes too busy to even talk and doctors are just the same. It wasn't always like that. When I was a young doctor I had plenty to do but there was time then to talk to the patients, time to get to know them. I can tell you I met a few characters in my time on the wards and I had time in those days to get to know some of them very well.

Generally speaking the Irish are a talkative people, always ready to crack a joke or have a laugh, ready to take whatever life throws at them but sometimes this laid back attitude can hid real concerns or worries.

When I qualified I had learned enough about medicine to practice but I still had a lot to learn about people. I started doing that in my first job. It was one of those soft sunny days in July when I went to see a patient called John Barnett. I was working in a Dublin teaching hospital and had been there all of three weeks.

John had been losing weight. There didn't seem to be anything wrong with him except he seemed to be getting thinner by the day. "I've lost over a stone and a half in the last three months," he told me. "I don't know why, I eat like a horse and feel as fit as a fiddle. I have neither ache nor pain".

I took a detailed history and examined John carefully. I was still very new to the job and began to think I was missing something when I couldn't find anything wrong with him. I couldn't make a diagnosis. John needed some tests and to be seen by a consultant. I explained this to him and he seemed quite satisfied.

In fact he seemed relaxed and pleased to be sitting up in bed looking round at the other patients in the ward. One of the first things I noticed about him was that he liked to talk. Irish people like a good story and they are good talkers but if there had been an examination in talking, then John would have taken top marks. It was one of those days when there was very little that needed doing and I sat at the side of his bed and listened to him. He had a lilt to his voice that gave a rhythm and music to his words, Yet there was an alertness in his manner that told me the man was no fool.

He was fifty-three years old and had spent his whole life working in insurance. He joined the firm when he was sixteen and had stayed with them ever since. He had worked in different branches and was eventually transferred to the main claims office and stayed there ever since.

"It suited me fine," he said. "I worked just hard enough to satisfy my boss. I didn't work too hard or too little and that way I avoided promotion. I could have got promotion if I'd worked a bit harder but there's plenty of those sort of people about who always want to do better. They can have their promotion as far as I am concerned"

"We were at the firm's Christmas party one year and some of those lads had drunk a bit more than was good for them. The senior partner put his arm round my shoulder and blasted sherry fumes into my face. He told me that I didn't have enough initiative or go in me to make the grade. He wouldn't have understood even if he'd been in an understanding sort of state. All I wanted was an easy life and enough free time to do what I really wanted."

"That seems a strange attitude to life," I told him with all the wisdom of a twenty-three year old. "If you'd worked harder and got promoted you would have had a better salary and more interesting work. Did you feel at the time, John, that you would be under too much pressure in a higher position?"

"Pressure, my eye. I was under ten times more pressure the way I operated then than I would have been if I had gone for the top job in the company."

"Is that right?" I said looking at him and wondering what on earth he was talking about.

"You bet it is," he said. "I kept the same job all the time because I knew it inside out. I could have done it in my sleep. I started work at nine o'clock on the dot and I had it all done by lunchtime. That left me free to do what I liked in the afternoon. I would fill in a form or two to give the impression that I was still working."

"But didn't you get bored, sitting there twiddling your thumbs all those afternoons, John?"

"Bored?" he exclaimed, "Bored, that isn't as word in my vocabulary. I had plenty to do. I was studying."

"Studying?" That was something here I didn't understand. John Barnett didn't look an academic with his florid face and his bright twinkling eyes. "Were you thinking of taking exams and going to University?"

He laughed aloud at the thought. "All that studying them students do and some of them ending up with less of a salary than I was earning in the insurance office. Not on your life. I had no notion of being a student I was studying the form."

"The form?"

"Aye, doc, the form. You must know what the form is. You can't be that ignorant with all your education. Horses, doctor, that's what I studied, horses. I read every newspaper, every book, every article and magazine ever written about horses. I spent four or five hours every day reviewing and studying them, every day for the last thirty odd years. I reckon I know more about any horse that ever appeared on any starting line at any racecourse in England or Ireland for the past twenty-five years than any other man alive."

I didn't know what to say. I had seen men gathered round the bookies on race afternoons and the excitement when one of them won something big, but John didn't fit in with their image. John seemed somehow different. "You must be very interested in horses," was all I could think of to say.

"Interested in horses?" he said with a snort, "I have as much interest in horses as I have in that chair," and he pointed to an old armchair that had been pushed into the corner of the ward since the First World War.

"Why do you want to read so much about horses then John if you aren't interested in them?"

"I'll tell you why. When I was a young boy I discovered two things. One was that I had a photographic memory and the second was that winning a bet gave me the greatest thrill I ever experienced. Let me explain to you. My father was a gambler. He would go down to the pub on a Saturday afternoon, have a few pints and go along to the bookies. I'll tell you one thing about him - he never won too much. He'd come back without a penny in his pocket and it would be bread and water for me ma and the rest of us six children for the rest of the week. He would have a big win on the odd occasions and we would have fish and beef for a few days until the drink and betting caught up with him again. We weren't any different to the other families in the street. It was a way of life in those days.

Anyway, I was a reader from as early as I can remember. I never had to be taught. I taught myself, I bet that surprises you. There wasn't much to read in our house. I would read anything I could find from the labels on a can of beans to the instruction manual which came with our wireless. I would read the newspapers when we had one, I would read them from cover to cover several times over but I liked the bits about the horse racing the best. I think that was the only part my father read and they would be marked and well thumbed. The more I read about the horses the more I began to visualise a pattern of race winners in my mind. I could have almost told my father before he went out what horses to bet on that day but I daren't say a word. I would only have got a clip round the lughole for my trouble if I had.

Saturday was not a good day to confront my father, but there was one Saturday when I was convinced I could name three winners who were running that day at Ferryhouse. I just had to tell him. No matter what he did I just knew those horses were going to win. I asked him to put my two shillings life savings on a treble. He shouted at me and cuffed me round the ear before stomping out.

"Don't you think one gambler's enough in this house?"

"He put his whole weeks wages on that treble, the whole two pounds and the horses won. He came home with four hundred pounds in his cap. He gave three hundred and fifty pounds to my mother and told her that she was never to let him touch it no matter what happened. It was the first time we had any kind of security in our home. Mother was careful with it mind you but there was always food on the table for a long time after that.

My father never said a word to me about the win. He carried on betting and drinking and finished in the debtors' prison because of betting losses and he wouldn't let my mother bail him out. Then when he was fifty, he stopped betting,. He told me that for the first time in his life, he felt at peace with him.

Seeing my father win that bet gave me a terrific buzz that lasted for months. I decided there and then that this was what I wanted to do when I grew up. I wanted to be a gambler. I couldn't tell my mother I wanted to gamble. She'd had enough to put up with my father, so I looked for a job where I could earn a wage and carry on with my betting on the quiet, my real career as a punter. When I got to a certain level in the company, I decided that was as far as I wanted to go. Anything higher would have meant executive responsibility and that was what I wanted to avoid, too time consuming altogether."

I glanced at my watch, I did have other patients to see, yet something in John's voice, his manner, captivated me. I didn't move. He went on to explain how he had studied every horse, trainer and jockey that had raced over the last twenty five years.

I thought of this man leaning against the pillow as if he didn't have a care in the world and wondered at his knowledge. I had just completed five years of intensive medical training and had such a feeling of achievement when I completed my finals, as if I had reached a pinnacle of knowledge, yet I didn't know a fraction of what John Barnett did.

He had studied books about veterinary science that were on the library shelves so that he could understand the horses' anatomy and further his knowledge of them. He had studied geology and how the weather could affect the racetrack and whether the racetracks were clay or sand, if they were porous or heavy and suited the horse that he favoured. He learned all about meteorology to help him predict the weather on race days and if the prevailing conditions would upset "his horse".

I could have listened to John for hours but I had work to do. Even as I stood up to leave he still chatted on with that soft musical brogue of his. He had the real gift of the gab.

"And you know," he said. "It is a funny thing, even at the end of all that study, I was never particularly fond of horses. I respected them, mind you, but a horse is still a horse to me and I know more about them than the greatest horse lover who ever lived."

I tried to drag myself away but even as I took my first step back with the words of an excuse on my lips he said something that caught my attention right away.

"Now, if you look at the Grand National, I made a few bets on that race myself in my time and lost every brass farthing in my early days. It's one race you have to study very very carefully or you're on the road to nowhere.

Before the National, or any other big race come to that, I had to know everything that there was to know about the horse I was thinking of backing and of the conditions on the course. Lady Luck does play a part, I'll give you that.

Look at 1966 in the Grand National when all the front runners fell at Beechers Brook and Foinavon, a no hoper, came from the back to win at 100-1. Nobody could have predicted that. I didn't bet that day, didn't like the weather conditions for the horse I fancied. It was an effort to keep my money in my pocket I can tell you. But that's the difference between a gambler and a real punter. Even then I thought I had got it wrong. My horse was a length or two in front of the others until they nearly all fell at Beechers Brook. I'm telling you I was mighty glad I hadn't bet then."

I sat down on the edge of his bed again. I told John I thought his story was fascinating.

"Fascinating, my eye," he said. "It was an awful strain. I don't know if I would do the same again. Living like that is full of deception and double dealing. When I lived at home with my mother, I never took a thing home to do with horse racing. I didn't want to upset her. I respected her too much after all she had been through. She never suspected a thing. Even when I got married I told the wife that I liked to go to the Curragh or Cheltenham with a few friends and we might have a quiet bet or two. I came home from Cheltenham once with £20,000 pounds in my pocket and gave her £200. She was as pleased as punch with me.

It made up my salary to the pay I would have received if I'd taken promotion at work and I made a point of never asking my friends at work home in case my wife talked about the money I was earning. It was a dual existence but the excitement of winning made it all worth while for me. A few big losses in the early days nearly put me to the wall but I made over £200,000 and the family wanted for nothing. I have invested the money for them. They will get it when I die. Not bad for a double existence is it?" he added with a grin. "Better than any of your 007 agent stuff".

I really had to go and catch up with my other admissions. I shook his hand and left, my mind reeling with the story of his extraordinary double life.

The morning after John's admission Dr. Brandon Fitzmorris, the consultant arrived at 9am on the dot to do his ward round. He was an authoritarian of the old School.

He had been educated at an English Public school before going on to study at Cambridge. He joined the RAMC during the Second World War and was captured in France in 1940. Five years in a German prisoner of war camp had done little to bring him out of himself.

He seemed to look down on everybody with a look on his face that suggested he could sense an unpleasant smell. He always wore the same charcoal grey suit, white shirt and a Cambridge University tie. I never saw him wear anything different.

He disliked anything that was German or Italian as a result of his war experiences although he extended this dislike to include the Russians, the French, the Americans and anyone else who disagreed with him. On one ward round a pretty female medical student coyly asked him if he would prefer to drive a Mercedes or a Ferrari car.

He drew himself up to his full height. He was a tall man. Looking down his nose at her he replied, "Madam, why would I want any of that foreign material when I have a perfectly good Bentley to see me about?"

When Dr. Fitzmorris came onto the ward he walked with such an air of confidence that the patients felt that he owned the ward, which he did in part. His great grandfather had paid to have the hospital built and both his father and grandfather had been consultants there. He had an aura about him that this was a world he owned from the first time he stepped into the hospital as a medical student.

A retinue of junior doctors, registrars, nurses, medical students and nursing students followed silently and dutifully behind him when he entered the ward. When he began the ward round nobody was permitted to speak unless Dr. Fitzmorris addressed them directly and that included the patients. The only exception to this rule was the ward sister, sister McSwiggan, and a right battle-axe she was too.

He was methodical in everything he did. He would stand at the end of the bed while his followers gathered round, no one daring to get too close to the great man. He would glance briefly at the temperature chart and the patient's name and without looking at the patient would nod to his houseman. That was the houseman's cue to begin his presentation about the patient and his illness. The houseman had to give the patient's illness briefly and succinctly and describe any clinical findings. On no account was he to make a diagnosis. Sometimes Dr. Fitzmorris would ask a curt question or two before silently musing to himself. Occasionally he would examine the patient's abdomen or take his stethoscope from his pocket and briefly apply it to the patient's chest. Then he would straighten up and clear his throat. This was the big moment. Dr. Fitzmorris was about to make a diagnosis and, nine times out of ten, he would not have given the patient more than a cursory glance. He would make his pronouncements with authority.

"This man has cirrhosis, probably secondary to haemochromatosis," or, "This lady clearly has early features of motor neuron disease."

I was always amazed at how accurate his diagnosis was. He rarely got it wrong. He once said, "You know gentlemen, (he always ignored women doctors and refused to employ them saying they should be at home looking after their husbands) you are a good clinician when you can walk through a ward and diagnose each patient from the end of the bed without speaking to them." He was a good advertisement for this method.

On this particular morning Dr. Fitzmorris approached John's bed and took up his position without so much as a glance at him.

The retinue dispersed neatly and soundlessly to their positions. Dr. Fitzmorris inclined his head as a sign for me to begin. I briefly presented the salient points of my examination and investigations. When I finished Dr. Fitzmorris began to clear his throat, the prelude to his diagnosis, when John's voice suddenly boomed out.

"Good morning, good morning, Dr. Fitzmorris and all present here today. How are you all this fine Summer's morning?"

A gasp of astonishment escaped from the retinue. Dr. Fitzmorris recoiled as if he had been struck. He glared angrily at John. In his twenty years as a consultant nobody had ever interrupted him in that way before, certainly not a patient and certainly not just as he was about to proclaim his diagnosis.

"Are you speaking to me, sir?" he demanded obviously outraged by John's brashness.

"Indeed I am, Dr. Fitzmorris, Indeed I am. You're the man I'm speaking to." John was not one bit put out by the icy reception to his questions.

"I thought we should at least say hello to each other Dr Fitzmorris, before you plonked your hands on me," John added with a smile.

There was a sharp intake of breath from the onlookers. Sister McSwiggan looked at John as if she could have choked him. She tried to put a hand over his mouth to keep him quiet but he pushed it to one side and continued.

"Do you think you will be able to get me fixed up by Saturday, Dr. Fitzmorris? There is a big race meeting I would like to go to."

For the first time ever, I saw Dr. Fitzmorris rendered speechless.

"This is most unprecedented sir," he eventually spluttered when he found his voice. The rest of us stood watching in silence, wondering how the great man was going to react to somebody else actually raising their voices in his presence. "This is really quite out of order, Mr. Barrett".

"I know it is Dr. Fitzmorris. I know it is and I'm very sorry if I have offended you in any way, but I heard you were a great man at making the quick and accurate diagnosis. If you don't mind I would like you to make a diagnosis of what's wrong with me and tell me right here and now. Have I got cancer is what I want to know and if I have, how long do you think I have to live?"

We were all aghast by John's behaviour and at the same time enthralled as Dr. Fitzmorris' face turned a shade of purple. The veins stood out on his forehead and his eyes seemed to bulge from his head. He was so taken aback by John's attitude that he had difficulty finding his voice.

"This is most irregular, Sir, this line of questioning, most irregular," he eventually managed to say. "I have never come across anything like it before in my life. Never! I have to say I am quite appalled by your manner. However, as you seem so insistent Mr.

Barnett that I tell you what is wrong with you, I will tell you to the best of my knowledge. From the information given to me, it would appear that you almost certainly have cancer of the pancreas. It is more than likely that this cancer has spread to your liver and possibly to the bones of your vertebrae."

"That doesn't sound too good from my point of view, does it Dr. Fitzmorris?" John said quietly, "but at the same time I would like to thank you for being so straight with me. The truth about my condition is exactly what I wanted to know. I have one last question I would like to ask you and I am sorry to be so persistent. But, could you please tell me how long do you think I have to live?"

Dr. Fitzmorris looked at John very crossly. He didn't care to be cross-examined by anyone and certainly not by a patient.

"Really, Mr. Barnett, this is completely out of order. I am not God Almighty. I cannot predict anyone's life span and I certainly cannot tell you how long you have to live."

"With all due respect Dr. Fitzmorris, I appreciate you are not the Almighty and I am not expecting miracles from you," John said very gently, "But could you please tell me to the best of your knowledge as an experienced physician, what you think my prognosis is?"

"Very well, Mr. Barnett, if you insist, but I have to say I cannot agree to your line of questioning for one moment. However, as you are so persistent, I will tell you to the best of my knowledge. You will probably live three months, six at the maximum.

"Thank you very much Dr. Fitzmorris. That is exactly what I needed to know," John said as he lay back on the pillows.
Dr. Fitzmorris did not say another word. He turned on his heels and stalked out of the ward.

I went to see John later on and asked him what all the crazy carry on had been about.

"You really did rub Dr. Fitzmorris up in the worst possible way, John. I know he can be fussy but he is the best physician I have ever come across. If anyone can help you he can. There is no point in annoying him. He would have explained everything to you and your family in his own time."

"I'm sorry if I caused you or the doctor any inconvenience but I am a betting man as you know. I like to have the facts in front of me so that I can put my life in order. Dr. Fitzmorris didn't seem to be in any hurry to give me the information I needed to know. I want to place one very big bet before I die but it is essential I know how long I have to live before I can do it."

He wouldn't say another word about the matter and signed himself out of the hospital that evening. He told me before he left that he had a lot of business to see to and he didn't seem to have a lot of time to do it in.

I saw him six weeks later in the out-patient department and was surprised to see how well he was doing considering the advanced stage of his disease. He told me that two weeks earlier he had made the biggest and most important bet of his life.

"What do you think of that James?" he asked with a twinkle in his eye.

"I don't know John," I said doubtfully. "Do you think it is a good idea putting on a large bet at this stage of your life, especially with your outlook. You could leave your family without any money after your death if you are not careful."

"Don't worry about that, they'll be alright. I've left them plenty of money. I couldn't get at the money now even if I wanted to. I have won more than £200,000 over thirty years and they will be getting most of that. The wife won't know anything about it until after I am dead. How do you think I'm doing anyway?" he asked suddenly changing the subject.

"Do you not think I am doing extra well for someone with pancreatic cancer. Shouldn't I nearly be on my death bed at this stage?" he asked with a grin.

"I must admit, I never expected to see you looking so fit," I told him and he smiled with pleasure.

"I tell you why I asked you that but you are to keep it to yourself.

I don't want anyone else to know. I am no hypochondriac and I am not afraid of dying. I know my time is almost up, even if it is a bit premature for my liking. I have to make the best of the time I have left without whinging if I can so I'll tell you what I have done to keep my interest at a maximum. I took out a bet with five lads that I know. They are the sort of lads who would bet £20 on two flies sitting on a wall to see which one would fly off first. I put £50,000 up against them. If I live until the 1 June, I win £250,000 from them and if I die before then, they get my £50,000 between them."

"You can't be serious making a bet like that John? The chances of you living until next June are almost nil." I had blurted it out before I realised what I was saying. Cancer treatment in those days was nothing like it is today and pancreatic cancer can be a particularly malignant type of cancer which was, virtually untreatable then.

"How on earth did you get them to take a bet like that anyway?" I asked trying to hide my blunder.

John smiled. "Thank you for being so honest with me, even if it was unintentional. I showed the lads copies of my insurance reports, which gave them my diagnosis. I went to the medical library and looked up the textbooks and found out about cancer of the pancreas. It said that people with this type of cancer generally had three months to live after the time of diagnosis and maybe up to six months. I gave the lads copies of that.

When those lads read my reports and realised that I was aiming to live for ten months, they were nearly tripping over themselves to put on their bets."

I still didn't think it was a wise thing for him to do and told him so.

"Wise?" he queried. "What has wisdom to do with it anyway? If I had spent my life being wise, I wouldn't have had half the enjoyment I have had. I spent my whole life taking a chance, and in any case, isn't it better I go out with a bang rather than sitting around feeling miserable and waiting to die. This has given me an incentive to keep going and I'll tell you something, I am going to try and make it. It is all up to me now. It is not like trying to guess if a race is fixed or figuring out the form of a horse and the mood of the jockey or any other innumerable permutations that occur in every race. It is all up to me and how I can fight this thing," and he tapped himself in the region of his stomach.

"It is a test of my own courage. Am I going to be able to hold on?"

He paused for a few seconds to gather his breath. He was obviously excited about the prospect of this last bet.

"Did you ever read Rudyard Kipling's poem, 'If'," he continued with some emotion. "That was all about holding on, and "Yes you can be a man my son", I am in there with him holding on. I want to be that man."

"Never mind Kipling." I said a little sharply to try and bring him back to reality. "What does your wife think of all this?"

"She never said a word."

"Never said a word?" I repeated astonished at her fortitude.

"Aye, because I never told her," he replied with a laugh.

There was no point in arguing with a man like that who had worked everything out for himself and had all the answers.

"Even if you do win, John, how can you be so sure the other men will pay up. You'll probably be too ill to get the money off them."

"The bet has been laid now James, for better or worse. I have thought of all that. We went to a solicitor and he holds the money - until pay day."

The weeks and months went by and John reached the fifth month looking remarkably fit but, in the seventh month he had begun to lose weight and he was getting weaker. His spirits were as high as ever though and he often talked about how he was going to blow his pile of money on his friends when he won the bet, just as long as he could keep going. They were all going to fly to Monte Carlo and stay at the Carlton Hotel for a week and have a last fling at the casinos there.

Two weeks short of his deadline, John was admitted to hospital in a very poor condition. I had moved onto another hospital to continue my training by this time so I was no longer looking after him medically. I went to visit him. I was fascinated by his story and the two of us had become good friends. I admired his fighting spirit and his total lack of self-pity.

"Thanks for coming to see me, James," gritting his teeth as a spasm of pain went through him. "I'm afraid I'm going to lose this bet, my biggest ever. It was a good race though. I nearly won it. I have enjoyed every minute of it. What would Kipling have said of me now, hanging on like that. I can't hang on any more, no matter how much I want to."

"Well, John", I said with some emotion. "I can tell you one thing. You won that race by a mile."

He died the next morning, one week and six days short of his biggest ever win.

POST SCRIPT

Three months after John's death, I received a letter from his solicitor. It contained five £20 notes and a short letter from John.

Dear James,

When you get this letter, I will have been dead and buried for three months. I want you to blow this money on enjoying yourself on two conditions that aren't binding.

The first is, say a prayer for me once in a while and the second is easier. Bet £10 on a horse that I have been following for the last two years with some interest - Red Rum. That horse will win the Grand National at least twice and probably a third time. Give him until 1973 and he will be in the top three. And you know what? I'll be the first man to lay a bet from beyond the grave. Won't that be a record? What would Dr. Fitmorris say about that?

Your friend
John.

Red Rum won the Grand National in 1973 for the first time at very good odds. I hadn't placed a bet on him. I wasn't that interested in horses and betting and I had forgotten the Grand National was on. I didn't make the same mistake in 1974. I put £20 pounds on Red Rum. He won at 11/1. That was the second of his three wins.

GEORGE

I knew that the teaching hospital in Central Dublin was the one for me as soon as I laid eyes on it. It was built of grey stone and stood at the end of a long, leafy avenue but it was the interior of the building that was most impressive. The wards were spacious with large windows which looked out over the city and out as far as the Irish Sea. The entrance to the main building was up a sweeping granite stairway and through oak and glass doors into a large entrance hall.

The first thing that struck you when you entered was the size and feeling of space that enveloped you when you went in. It was awe inspiring yet welcoming. There were two huge fireplaces and, in the winter months, roaring fires blazed in them. Just looking at them was enough to warm you. A circular stone staircase grandly swept up three floors from the entrance hall to the high ceiling. An old, clanking lift creaked up and down in the central space of the stairs. Just inside the door was a huge mahogany table and two chairs. They were near enough the fire to feel the warmth of it, yet far enough away to prevent a roasting. Behind this mahogany table sat George.

George was the head hospital porter.

I first visited the hospital when I was a second year medical student and the first person I saw when I entered the premises was George. I thought then that he was an old man, but the more I got to know him, the younger he seemed to grow. It was difficult to judge exactly how old he was but, I suppose, at that time, he must have been in his mid fifties.

George knew everything there was to know about the hospital and nearly everything about all the people who worked there. Within three days of a medical or nursing student entering the main doors, George would know their name, where they came from, where their father worked and how much he earned and, often, a lot more besides. He had no computer to guide him but he didn't need one. He knew every patient that came through the door, what ward he was in and what was wrong with him.

George took his position very seriously. You only had to glance at him sitting at the huge mahogany table in the entrance hall as visiting hour approached to realize that.

He was a man of medium height but very well built with extraordinary square shoulders. He had been in the British navy when he had been younger where he had been a keen boxer and swimmer. He wasn't exactly a keep fit fan but he was determined to keep himself fit by walking the three miles to work each day and back again in the evening. He refused to use the lift to the top floor unless he was taking a patient to the wards. He preferred to use the stairs as a healthy alternative.

He was always immaculately dressed and his hair was trimmed almost to the skull above his square, muscular face. He always wore a white shirt and waistcoat and a neatly knotted tie. I once saw him wearing an academic tie and asked him where he had got it.

"Harrow on the Hill, James old man," he said with a broad wink, "my alma mater."

That was one of the problems with George. The expression on his face never changed and you were never sure if he was telling the truth or just joking.

Somehow George always managed to wear a smartly pressed porter's green coat without a tear or a spot on it. If the coat had been a white one, he could easily have been mistaken for a doctor, in fact, I often wondered if some of the patients didn't think he was one of the medical staff. He never did anything to change that idea if they did.

"Having a busy one, James?" he would shout at me when he saw me racing across the hallway and up three flights of stairs to answer a crash call. He spoke in a clipped military voice with a slight Irish twang to it

A Spoonful of Medicine

He had a habit of rising himself onto his toes as he spoke and inclining his head forward with a quizzical look on his face when he asked a question. It seemed as though he was putting his whole body and soul into the situation. He was a very intense man. He had a job to do and he was doing it to the best of his ability.

Visiting hours were carefully regulated in those days and, in the early evening, as the hour approached, George would wait in the entrance hall in front of the fire with his hands behind his back watching the coming and going of the medical staff but he would sit behind his desk as the visitors began to arrive, directing them genially and efficiently in the right direction.

"Jim's on the mend, Mrs Boland," he'd say to a wee worried woman as she came through the door with an anxious look on her face. "He's out of intensive care and in Ward seven."

"How's Fred tonight," another woman would ask as she came into the entrance hall, her voice sounding anxious.

"To tell you the truth, love," he would say very gently, "Fred's had a bad day, I'm sorry to say. He seems to have had a bit of a setback but the doctors are working on him.

Everybody got on well with George. Everybody loved him and George loved everybody. But he had a special admiration for the senior consultant surgeon, Mr Henry Joy McCracken. (The junior staff always referred to him as Mr McCrackers.)

George had served under him in the Second World War. They had been on the same ship. It had been hit by a torpedo and George had nearly lost a leg and he always attributed the fact that he hadn't to McCracker's treatment

Henry Joy was a big shambling man whose shoulders had begun to stoop with age. He had white bushy eyebrows and a mane of white hair above his long, cadaverous face. Henry knew he was a good surgeon but he also knew his limitations and didn't mind admitting them. When he taught us medical students, he never tired of saying in his lugubrious voice, "Always remember one thing if you remember anything – Common things are common. Always look for the simple diagnosis. Common sense is not as common as you might think. For the rest of your lives, your bread and butter will be in the coughs, the appendices, the stomach ulcers, the sore throats and the head-aches, so don't go looking for beri-beri or elephantiasis in the middle of Dublin."

He repeated himself so often over the years and kept everything so simple that I still clearly remember his rules of three or four all these years later..

"Rule of three," he'd say, "when you examine a patient's joint there are three things to do – look, feel, move. You look at the joint, you feel it and then you move it."

He would pause to emphasize each word.

"Rule of four," he would continue. "If a man has a pain in his upper abdomen, he almost always has one of four things, gastritis, gallstones, pancreatitis or heart disease. Rule of four again, you do four investigations – a barium meal to rule out the stomach, a cholecystogram to rule out the gall bladder, a blood test for raised Amylase to rule out the pancreas and an electocardiographic tracing to rule out the heart. If these show nothing, you have three choices. You get another opinion, you open him up or you send him home."

Sometimes Henry Joy would be called over to the Accident and

Emergency Department if there was a difficult or unusual case to deal with. You could see him standing there going through the lists in his mind – rule of four, pain in the lower abdomen, appendicitis, cystitis, diverticulitis or bowel spasm, which one is it? He would make a quick decision and move on to the next patient.

I always liked it when he was the consultant covering the A. and E. Department. He would come to see the patient shortly after he had been called. He wouldn't keep us waiting like some of the more pompous surgeons did. They seemed to measure their importance by the amount of inconvenience they could cause us lesser mortals and by how long they could keep us waiting. Henry Joy was never like that. We knew that if there was an emergency, he would come straight away and, often, George would be following along behind him as if to make sure he didn't get lost on the way, walking in exactly the same manner with his hands clasped behind him and his body leaning forward from the waist and placing each step at the same time and at the same distance from each other.

Sometimes he would follow Henry Joy into the cubicle but, if Sister McNeil was on duty, he would often come out again pretty smartly. We were never sure if the good doctor knew that George was behind him. He never made any sign to suggest that he knew he was there.

McCrackers was a great educator. He always educated everyone around him. He couldn't help it. It was second nature to him. If he was looking at a Chest X-ray, he would say, "Rule of four. What are the four things we're looking for here, doctor?"

Then he'd tell you the answer without waiting for a reply, rapidly pointing it out by tapping the X ray with his pen, that is if George didn't jump in with the answer first. Henry Joy never liked to embarrass anyone or show them up because they didn't know the answer.

If George ever had a free moment, he would come over to the Accident and Emergency Department. He loved the excitement and buzz of the place and the banter of the staff. Once he left the main building and started towards the A.and E. department, his personality would undergo a metamorphosis. A twinkle would appear in his eye yet he somehow managed to maintain his air of gravity.

He would often take up his position at the entrance to the department, looking every bit like a sergeant major ready to shout out an order. Ramrod straight, he would scrutinize every patient that went through the door. We didn't take a lot of notice of him or what he was doing until one day, I heard him greet an elderly man at the door.

"Good evening, Sir. May I be of some assistance to you? What seems to be the problem?"

The old man pointed at his stomach and made a retching sound.

"An abdominal condition, Sir. I think we've got the very man to assess your condition if you'd be so kind as to follow me."

George, after his quick scrutiny, ignored all the hospital protocol and marched right past the reception desk and showed the old man into a vacant cubicle. He asked him to lie down and checked his pulse.

"I'll get the doctor to look at you immediately, Sir," he said and came out to look for a casualty doctor.

He saw me standing at the X ray screen. He came straight across to me and said, "I think we have an acute abdomen in cubicle three, James, an appendix by the look of things, a bit of cutting experience for young Henry Joy.

Four hours later, a nasty looking appendix was removed without the assistance of George I might add.

One thing that was anathema to George was bad manners or loutish behaviour. He absolutely detested rudeness. One evening when he was standing at his post by the Casualty Department door, a young man pushed his way in and demanded to be seen straight away. He wouldn't take no for an answer and became quite aggressive.

I was on duty that night and I was surprised to see George getting a bit red in the face. The ever courteous George was looking hot and bothered under the collar. He began to look distinctly irritated when the patient made some insulting remarks about Sister McNeill. I could see George clenching and unclenching his fists and I thought for a second he was going to revert to some very basic principles to teach the young man some manners. However he controlled himself and saw that the best way to settle things down with the least trouble was to have the patient seen quickly and moved out of the department.

He lead the man to a cubicle and, turning, left abruptly, an expression of disapproval showing on his face. I went in to see to the patient who was complaining of a headache but, before I could question the man, George suddenly reappeared wearing a stethoscope round his neck.

"I believe this man has a troublesome headache, Professor," he said to me as he walked straight past and plonked his stethoscope forcefully against the man's head and pretended to listen to it.

I looked on in amazement, not sure how to deal with George in front of the patient. Before I could say anything, George turned to me and said, "I think we have a head case here, Professor, yes indeed, a very serious head case," He turned and walked out.

Several evenings later, the ambulance men brought a very drunk and disorderly woman into casualty. She had multiple lacerations to her head and legs after falling down a flight of stairs. The ambulance crew wheeled her into a cubicle where she lay shouting and screaming as she struggled to get off the trolley.

George suddenly appeared and, with a firm shove, pushed the trolley hard against the wall to stop the woman escaping. He stayed at the head of the trolley looking down at the dishevelled woman who was shrieking loudly as she struggled like an alley cat to get off the trolley. Two other porters came over and did all they could to stop her from injuring herself but they had to give up. She was uncontrollable.

I was on duty that night with Dr Simmons, the surgical registrar. He was a small intense man who was more at home playing the cello or reading philosophy than dealing with violent drunks. We wondered what we should do to calm this woman down so that we could treat her. Dr Simmons had failed to notice that George was still in the cubicle with the disruptive patient.

"I wonder if we should give her some intramuscular paraldehyde or an intravenous injection of diazepam to sedate her," Dr Simmons muttered to himself at a bit of a loss as to what he should do to calm this crazy woman down.

She was so drunk that we were worried that we would compromise her breathing if we gave her a large sedative. We could have finished up killing her. As the two of us were standing there wondering what would be the best treatment in the circumstances, George suddenly spoke up.

"Gentlemen, these types of individuals are very disruptive and difficult to manage. It's hard to control this sort of behaviour don't you think, Dr Simmons?"

"I do indeed," Dr Simmons answered absent mindedly as he looked at the woman. He was totally distracted by her screaming and wild behaviour. His brow was furrowed as he weighed up the risks of trying to sedate her against the risk of her injuring herself or somebody else if she continued to throw herself around so violently.

"I find an intramuscular injection of Largactil excellent in these cases."

"An injection of Largactil, you say," Dr Simmons repeated to himself. "That's exactly what the woman needs, a shot of Largactil."

George slipped out of the cubicle as Dr Simmons prepared and administered the injection. I don't think he ever realized that he was acting on advice that had been given to him by the head porter.

George's best ever performance came late one night when everyone in the A and E Department was tired after a particularly heavy day, though the day was by no means over.

A man was brought in who had been involved in a road traffic accident He was complaining of chest pains and was a little short of breath. We were still hectically busy and, as there were no doctors free at that moment, a fourth year medical student was sent to examine him. He was unable to find anything wrong with the patient but, as he was short of breath, he sent him for an X ray. George wheeled him across to the X ray department and brought him back a short time later with the X ray in its folder tucked under his arm.

One of the casualty doctors went across to see the man with the student beside him. By this time the pressure on the casualty staff was immense. We had just been told that multiple casualties from a car pile up was on their way to us in a fleet of ambulances. We were already full to overflowing and we had to clear as many patients as quickly as we could out of the department.

The doctor applied his stethoscope to the patient that George had taken for an X ray, then went across to look at the X ray. As he scanned it, he muttered that he couldn't see too much wrong. There were no broken bones or obvious signs of a serious lung injury. "I think we should give him some pain killers and send him home."

I had just come out of a cubicle and I could see George standing quietly behind the doctor looking at the X rays. I wondered what on earth he was up to. I could see him staring intently at the screen. George loved X rays especially when McCracken was examining them and giving out one of his rules of three or four.

"Excuse me, Gentlemen," George interrupted. "Rule of four, rule of four if my memory serves me right. We look for four things when examining an X ray, bony fractures, enlargement of the heart, clarity of the lungs and displacement of the trachea."

It might have been McCracken himself sounding off, it sounded so authentic. As he spoke, George tapped the X ray peremptorily in two areas with a pen before turning on his heel and striding off, shoulders hunched as if to say that it was nothing to do with him if doctors wanted to make fools of themselves.

The junior casualty doctor stared at the disappearing back with incredulity and then looked over to me. I shrugged my shoulders. He turned and looked at the X ray again, and then put his head forward and studied it a bit more closely.

"The man's right," I heard him tell the student, "would you look at that! There's a pocket of a air on the outside of the right lung and a slight displacement of the trachea."

The patient was admitted to hospital with a puncture of the lung and, after a chest drain had been inserted, he made a rapid recovery. George never mentioned the incident to anyone.

A few weeks before I left the hospital, the crash team was called to the front desk in the foyer. George had collapsed. I was one of the first to arrive and found him lying in great pain near the dying embers of the fire. Despite his pain, George made light of his condition.

"Rule of three, Dr Griffin," he said, "rule of three. I have one of three things, a very bad heart attack, a severe case of the gastrics or I shouldn't have smoked sixty cigarettes a day for the past forty years."

He was brought into the intensive care unit but, despite our best efforts, he died early the following morning.

The hospital was never quite the same again.

DR MOORE

I thought I had got to know everything I needed to know to become a doctor at medical school but it wasn't until I started working that I began to be educated, started to know what life was all about. Until that time I had spent a relatively sheltered life, living at home with a professional background, (my father was a doctor), and, when I went to medical school, most of the other students came from a similar background to my own. Now I had to get to know and understand people. And they came from all walks of life. We met them all, the eccentrics, the jokers, the stoics, the whingers. I hadn't known that people like some of them existed but I learned quickly. I had to. Some were immediately likeable. Although I tried to hide my true feelings, there were some of them that I found hard to like and others that got on my nerves. Dr Moore was one of the latter and I'd never even met him.

I came across him when I worked in the Accident and Emergency Department. He had an enormous practice close to the hospital and frequently sent patients in for us to deal with. But they started to come in a bit too frequently for my liking. It seemed that if he was in a hurry to finish his surgery or if he was having a bad day and couldn't be bothered to see any more patients, he would send them along to us. Occasionally, the patient would bring a grubby, undated note, hastily written on a torn out page from a jotter and shoved into a cheap, brown envelope. It invariably said the same –"Please see and advise." It would be signed with a signature that was impossible to read. That was about the height of clinical information we would receive.

Dr Moore occasionally came into the hospital to see one of his patients, particularly if they were one of his racing buddies and that was where I met him the first time.

He was a small, bald man in his mid fifties with broad shoulders and a big stomach he had acquired from years of either celebrating or drowning his sorrows at winning or losing on the horses. He always wore the same clothes, a tweed jacket, check shirt and grey flannel trousers and a Royal College of Surgeon of Ireland tie. Horses were his life and nothing was allowed to stand in the way of this interest.

Despite being an astute and somewhat sly operator, there was something likeable about the man and although he exasperated me from time to time, I changed my first opinion of him.

One morning before I had met him, although I had heard plenty about him, he sent four patients into the casualty department, one after the other, all with trivial complaints.

One of the men needed two stitches in his scalp. There was nothing serious about the wound and Dr Moore could have easily done it himself. I felt peeved at having to do such a trivial procedure. especially as casualty was already bulging at the seams.

"Why can't Dr Moore stitch these heads himself instead of sending them over to us? You'd think we had nothing better to do," I complained to Sister McNeill.

I expected a sympathetic reply but I didn't get one.

"Come on, James," she said to me in a motherly kind of way, "don't be too hard on the poor man. Old Moore's not a bad sort. If you saw how much his patients think of him, you wouldn't think so badly of him. He gives us a bit of extra work, I'll give you that but he's very nice to us at Christmas."

"He would have to be very, very nice to me to make up for all the nonsense he sends in here," I muttered

I gave up complaining when I saw I was on my own. Nobody else grumbled about the extra work load and I had to admit that when Sister McNeill said someone was alright, they generally were.

As it happened, I was still working in casualty at Christmas, not that Christmas reduced our workload at all. It just seemed to bring in a greater variety of injuries. It so happened that we were at our busiest when Dr Moore pushed through the door carrying a huge hamper from Brown Thomas's store for Sister McNeill. From his pockets and other parts of his person, he produced lesser gifts for the staff nurses.

"Huh," I thought, "the crafty old dodger. There he goes keeping in with the nurses. No wonder they don't object to the extra work. He doesn't give the likes of me a thought. He knows we're only here for six or twelve months before we move on."

Dr Moore had a cup of tea with the nurses and I could hear the laughter and high spirits coming from their direction while I was trying to stitch the top of yet another head. "Why do men always cut the crown of their heads when they fall over?" I muttered to myself feeling distinctly disgruntled as not a single nurse came to assist me. They were too busy dancing attendance on Dr Moore.

On his way out, he came over and shook my hand and said, "I would like to thank you for all your help over the past few months," and he handed me one of the grubby envelopes that generally contained one of his vague diagnoses.

"Not at all, Dr Moore," I said, "it was a pleasure."

At the same time, I was thinking that I was a hypocrite. What I should have been saying was that he was almost driving me crazy with all the work he was sending into us. I felt a real heel when I looked in the envelope. I was half expecting another one of his referral notes but, instead, I found two twenty pound notes and that, in the 1970s was a lot of money. I suppose it was after that that I started to get to know and understand the man a lot better, began to treat him more as a character than a nuisance.

I started to develop a suspicion that Dr Moore did not like the sight of blood. He lived by his own set of rules and one of them was that he never stitched wounds. "A complete waste of time," he told one of his cronies. "Why would I want to waste twenty minutes of my time stiching some thick eejits head when there's a hospital casualty department just down the road. Isn't it great experience for them young doctors up there anyway."

This rule was put to the test one morning when a German tourist on a cycling holiday round Ireland was knocked off his bike right outside Dr Moore's front door. He was a giant of a man with a mass of thick, blonde hair that had probably saved him from being more seriously injured. He lay on the road with blood pumping out of a scalp wound. His two cycling companions became increasingly concerned as their friend lay there looking dazed while the blood collected in a pool on the road..

"Bitte-sie mein Herr. Vere is zer ein doktor?" one of them asked a passer by who pointed to Dr Moore's brass name-plate six feet away from the injured man. The two men took hold of the man and dragged him into the waiting room. They were all big, blonde men, although Hans was the biggest and blondest of the three. They seemed to fill the dingy waiting room. Several patients were leaning against the wall waiting to see the doctor and, when they saw the state of the three men, they moved out of the room and formed a queue on the pavement.

Dr. Moore opened the door to see what the commotion was and came face to face with the three men who seemed to fill the room. He saw immediately that Hans wasn't very badly injured, despite the bleeding from his wound. His first thought was to get rid of the men as quickly as possible before they slowed down his high turnover rate.

"Gentlemen, please, please. This is not an Accident and Emergency room. Your friend is in urgent need of surgery. You must take him to the Emergency Department. It's only two hundred yards down the road," and he pointed in the direction of the hospital.

One of the young men, Jurgen said, "Hans is not, at zis time, able to valk to ze hospital, Herr Doktor."

Dr Moore said he would call an ambulance but Jurgen took hold of his arm. "Vill you please hev a look at Hans' head first, Herr Doktor?"

"I've seen all I need to see. Your friend is in a bad way and needs hospital attention."

"But Doktor, please to look at Hans' head first," and the two men virtually frog marched their friend into his surgery. They looked round the room for a couch but couldn't find one. "You hev no place to put Hans, Herr Doktor?" Big Jurgen was becoming almost as exasperated as Dr Moore who deeply resented this intrusion into his busy schedule.

"Put him on the floor over there," and he pointed to a very worn rug beside his desk. By this time, Hans had fully regained consciousness and was looking doubtfully round the pokey room and grimy floor with increasing concern. Despite his protests, his two friends lowered him to the floor and one of them put a rolled up coat under his head.

Dr Moore sat down at his desk and gave the wound a cursory glance. "It will need fifteen or twenty stitches at the very least," he said peremptorily.

"You will please to put in zese stitches Herr Doktor, yes?"

"If I have to I suppose I must but I'll need to get a few things ready first." He stood up and opened a dusty cupboard that was attached to the wall behind his desk. He took out a glass and a bottle of whisky and poured out a large measure.

"But, Herr Doktor, you are not giving Hans whisky. He does not drink," Jurgen said.

The doctor drank the glass back in one gulp. "Hans may not drink but I do, I need that to steady myself up before I tackle anything surgical," he said.

Dr Moore rubbed his hands with satisfaction when he told his friends about the speed with which those young men helped their friend up from the floor and made their way to the hospital down the road.

There was one thing that he could always find to do and that was take out teeth. Dr Moore loved extracting teeth. He said it was money for old rope. When he had been a student at The Royal College of Surgeons, he had struck up a friendship with a final year dental student who had, in return for a loan of ten pounds, shown him how to pull out teeth. Moore, ever the entrepeneur, saw the potential of adding this skill to his repertoire.

He pulled teeth at every opportunity and charged five shillings a time. He became so proficient that he could remove even the most stubborn of teeth in a matter of seconds. He would bring out a low seated, high backed chair for the purpose and ask the patient to sit on it.

"Sit down there now, Paddy like a good man," he would say, "on this special, hand carved dental chair of mine that I've had specially imported from the Far East would you believe. It was hand made by Tibetan monks especially to pull out Irish teeth." He wanted his patients to think they were getting their money's worth. If the truth was told, it was his old Granny's rocking chair, made in Coolock in North Dublin, which he took over when she died and cut off the rockers to make it stable. Dr Moore was always resourceful.

The low chair gave him enough leverage to pull the tooth and the high back allowed him to steady the patient's head. He never used anaesthetics, said they were a waste of time and a liability into the bargain. "The needle could hit a nerve Paddy and leave you with a numb jaw for the rest of your life and where would that leave us?

As Paddy lowered himself into the chair, Dr Moore would carry on with his patter. It was part of the extraction technique.

"You know, Paddy," he'd explain as he explored the open mouth, "pulling teeth is all about getting the patient to relax. That's all there is to it. Do you know how I found out, well, I don't expect you do but I'll tell you anyway.

"Now, when I was a young lad growing up in Clonakilty in the beautiful County Cork, I used to fish for trout in a nearby stream and I never caught a single fish and do you know why? I wasn't going the right way about it all. That's for why. I was spending half my time throwing out hooks with big juicy worms on them to them greedy fish when I should have been talking to them instead. Do you follow what I'm saying? Now you listen carefully to me. If ever you see a trout lying in shallow water, you have to talk to him in the right way to calm his nerves down. When you have him settled, you can tickle his belly.

"Tickling the belly soothes the nerves of a trout and puts him half to sleep and, before he knows what you're up to, you have him out of the water and half way to your dinner plate."

While he was talking, he would be finding the bad tooth and bringing up the pliers towards the mouth of the unsuspecting patient.

"Now then, Paddy, I can see you think all that talk of mine about fishing is a bit of old baloney. Am I right in saying so?"

As Paddy attempted to nod his head, not knowing whether he agreed or disagreed, the pincers would be clamped on to the tooth like a vice. There would be a tug from Doctor Moore and a grunt from Paddy.

"Put out your hand, Paddy, like a good man," he would say and the spluttering Paddy would do as he was told and the doctor would deposit the tooth with its enormous roots into his outstretched hand.

Occasionally, a stubborn tooth couldn't be budged. Dr Moore had a way for dealing with that as well.

"Get a good grip of that chair with your two hands, Paddy," he would say moving himself to face the patient at the same time. "Now open your mouth as wide as you can."

The pliers would be reapplied to the tooth. At the same time, Dr Moore would bring his knee up against the patient's chest, pinning him to the back of the chair. "Now this is going to hurt you about as much as it hurts me," he'd shout as he used his considerable bulk and strength to haul at the tooth as the unfortunate patient tried to struggle. There would be a grunt from the doctor and a roar from the patient - but the tooth would be out.

A steel bucket would be handed to the patient so that he could spit the blood into it. When they had both calmed themselves down, Dr Moore would hold the tooth up to the light and squint at it. "Do you think, Paddy, that I've pulled out the right tooth at all?"

Dr Moore's dental business flourished for years despite objections from the local dentists. Patients came from miles around to have their teeth extracted and none of them complained about their treatment.

When it was a race day, Dr Moore was in a hurry to get his surgery over quickly and get away down to a race meeting so that he could study the form and get his bets on before the afternoon racing in The Curragh or at Ferryhouse.

He had a big, old fashioned wireless in his consulting room and, if he wasn't able to get to an important race meeting or if he had put a particularly big bet on a horse, he would listen to the race in his surgery.

"I never saw anything like it," one of his patients told me, "the doctor listening to the wireless like that. He only had it on low when I went to see him one afternoon and it wasn't long before I realised he hadn't listened to one word I said. He kept glancing over at the wireless and, when the starter's orders were given, he was out of his chair like a jack in the box and across to the radio in a second. I carried on talking about my complaint in a half hearted sort of way because I could see that he had as much interest in me as the man in the moon. The doctor turned up the radio to full volume and looked at me crossly. 'Benedict,' he said, 'this is no time to be talking.'

The volume was up so high it made the wireless crackle. He pulled his chair over and sat with his ear hard against it. It was a wonder it didn't make him deaf. It gave me an ear-ache to add to all my other troubles. I never saw anything like the carry on that went on then.

Dr Moore was a picture of nerves and excitement as the horses got under way. The way he was jumping around you would have thought he was riding the horse himself. He rocked backwards and forwards and almost jumped out of the chair as they reached the jumps, raising himself right out of the chair as if he was taking the jump himself. When a horse went down, he'd glance sideways as if he was checking the positions of the other jockeys in the field and looking to see who was left in the race. I tell you, he wasn't listening to that race, he was living every minute of it.

By the time that race was finished, I was in a fair old lather myself, worrying about how his horse had done. He sat back in the chair. His face was as red as a beetroot and he was gasping for air. I thought that it would be me tending him rather than he advising me. But his horse had won. Suddenly he was on his feet, whooping like a child and slapping his thighs. He ran across the room to me and shook my hand and slapped me on the back. 'Well done, Benedict, well done,' he kept saying as if I was the jockey who had rode the winner rather than someone who needed help with the indigestion.

I couldn't help thinking that working yourself up over an 'ole animal couldn't be good for a body. Well, he pulled a five pound note from his pocket and shoved it into my hand. 'Get yourself away down to O'Leary's Lounge Bar Benedict like a good man," he said, 'and buy yourself a pint or two of stout and a packet of Woodbines. That will take your mind off that complaint of yours. It's mostly in your mind, anyway you know,' and he opened the door and almost shoved me out of it in his haste to get rid of me.

He's a great a doctor though is Doctor Moore. He was right about the stout and the fags too. That was the first thing that made me feel better. It settled the wind great. You should try it yourself when you feel a bit disturbed round the stomach."

When Dr Moore backed a winning horse, he was ecstatic. A loss left him in a bad mood that lasted for days. Fortunately he never married. I doubt if any woman could have coped with these mood swings, in any case, he wouldn't have had time for a wife. His whole life revolved round horse racing and the betting shop.

His surgery was just a means to an end. He had trimmed his clinical procedures and skills to the absolute minimum to expedite his surgery turnover. His first rule was that anything that was likely to take up time was to be referred immediately to the Accident and Emergency Department at the hospital.

Patients were not invited to sit down in his surgery for one reason. There was only one chair in there and he sat on it. In any case, the mere act of sitting down could take up valuable minutes and that slowed the turn around. Dr Moore sat with his back to the wall facing the door behind a simple table on which he kept a prescription pad, a book of sickness certificates and a stethoscopic which he called his miracle tubes. He kept no medical records. He knew all his patients from living and working in the same area as they did themselves. As soon as the patient entered the room, Dr Moore would look up, raise his eyebrows and say, "Yes, what is it, Jack."

"It's me lungs, Doctor, I've an awful cough........."

Before Jack could utter another word, Dr Moore would be out of his chair signalling for him to be quiet as he placed the miracle tubes on to his chest. He always placed the stethoscope on the outer most garment regardless of how many layers the patient was wearing. He didn't allow anyone to undress to be examined. It took up too much time and slowed down his turnover rate. If he had to write a prescription or a sickness certificate, he would write very quickly, hand them the necessary paper and be showing them the door before they had time to get into full flow.

"Now then, Mr Reilly, that chest of yours was in a bad way but I think I've caught it just in the nick of time. You take this prescription down to the chemist now like a good man. There's a great bottle in it which will have you on your feet in no time."

Before Mr Reilly knew what was happening, he was out of the surgery and the next patient was already in Dr Moore's room undergoing his rapid scrutiny. When he was taking blood pressure, Dr Moore did not bother with the arm cuff. That would have taken far too long.. He would put the stethoscope on the soft side of their elbow and, for a few seconds, he would listen intently.

"That blood pressure's excellent, Mrs McDermot," he told one lady. "I can't get over how you've come on since I gave you those tablets."

The problem was that Dr Moore's patients expected us to carry on in the same way and seemed to think we were at fault when we didn't. I discovered that one day when I had to treat Mrs McDermot in casualty. I went to take her blood pressure and she eyed me with great suspicion.

"Dr Moore never puts that thing round my arm." she said, "can you not do the same?"

"I'm sorry, Mrs McDermot," I said, "I'm not as experienced as

Dr Moore. I'm afraid I'll have to put the cuff on. But it won't hurt," I added when she looked at me with apprehension.

Dr Moore did get some awkward patients like the ones who had been to the hospital and seen how blood pressure was taken there and would ask him to do the same.

"Now, now, there's no need for that carry on, Jim," he would say reassuringly. When you've been in this business as long as I have, you can tell if someone has high blood pressure the minute they walk through the door."

His patients had great faith in him. They would accept his word and go away reassured. He certainly didn't want to set a precedent by putting on a blood pressure cuff. Use it for one patient and they would all want the same thing and that would have been disastrous to his time schedule.

He took a medical student on one year for teaching purposes. He thought he would get a few pounds for his trouble. He didn't. It was the last student he ever allowed into his surgery. The medical student told me that Dr Moore saw between sixty and seventy patients each morning in just under three hours. He had worked out that he was earning £90 in an average morning and that was a lot of money in those days.

He made a lot of money and he lost a lot as well, - on the horses. He lived on the edge in a perpetual state of excitement and anxiety and, eventually, his heart couldn't stand the strain. He developed angina which he diagnosed and treated himself. He wouldn't take time off to see a cardiologist.

He told one of his patients, "I've got a bad heart, Paddy. Do you see the first horse that makes me a big winner or a big loser come to that, well that animal will be the death of me," and it was.

He dropped dead from a heart attack one sunny afternoon at Cheltenham race course. He had bet £500 on a horse that had come in first at fifteen to one after a photographic finish. Dr Moore's heart couldn't stand it.

I was surprised at the people who were genuinely upset by his death. Despite his failings, he was liked by nearly everyone who knew him. Even though horses and betting dominated his life, he could be extremely generous and humorous. He was only too aware of his own failings. "I'm a flawed man," he told one of his racing cronies." I like horses and betting to a level that's not healthy but it's got such a grip on me that I've let the obsession run my whole life. Maybe I should have taken to the drink. It would have been cheaper in the long run."

Dr Moore's funeral was one of the biggest seen in Dublin for years. I was there myself. One of the mourners said to me at the grave side, "After that eulogy the priest gave old Moore, I'm wondering if they've buried the right man at all."

That about summoned Dr Moore up.

ROLY

Every Accident and Emergency Department has its regulars, mostly from the down and out brigade, and we were no exception. The Sister in charge, Sister McNeill, for all her toughness had a soft spot for drunks as long as they weren't disruptive. If the A. and E. department was quiet, she would let them sleep off their drink for a few hours or let them stay overnight if it was cold. One of the regular attenders that I met was Roly.

Roly was in his early 30s although he looked a lot older. He had been studying law when, as he put it, the drink got the better of me. He gave up his studies, or rather they gave him up. He was asked to leave. He began to drink seriously and, within two years, he was living on the streets, a hopeless alcoholic and a down and out.

Roly was tall and lean with a weather beaten face that had the bloated appearance of a chronic alcoholic. He had a bushy beard and long, straggly hair. He always wore the same clothes regardless of the weather. Even on the hottest summer day or a freezing cold winter night, he wore his blue shirt, baggy grey trousers and a threadbare, black, Crombie coat.

In all the time that I was in Dublin, both as a student and a doctor, I never remember seeing Roly sober. His drunkenness would vary from being pleasantly drunk, at which times he could be hilariously funny, to being so drunk that he couldn't stand up.

No matter how drunk he was, Roly was never unpleasant or rude. Because of this, we accepted him coming into the Accident and Emergency Department and, if things were quiet, we greatly enjoyed his good humour. There was something of the comic in Roly and, even in his drunken state, he knew he could make people laugh.

Roly spent the best part of the day drinking. He would drink

A Spoonful of Medicine

anything of an alcoholic nature that he could get his hands on from sparkling wine to methylated spirits. He told me that the worst drink he had ever had was a bottle of cheap perfume. There was nothing else to drink at that time and he took it as a last resort.

"I think I'll have to stick with Chanel number five in future doc, a superior brand," he told me in his slow cultured voice.

Roly was a very likeable man. He had a great interest in drama and the theatre which he had developed when he was at school and university in Oxford. He  had a beautiful rich, modulated voice which was very much out of keeping with his dishevelled appearance. On one occasion, when he wasn't as drunk as usual, I tried to talk to him.

"Roly, you're a very intelligent, personable man. Why don't you try and give up the drink and sort yourself out. Go and do something with yourself. I'm sure you could make something of yourself."

He looked at me sadly. "Ah, doctor," he said, "I'm disappointed in you. You're beginning to sound like my father. He always gave me that old line about giving up drink and doing something with my life. You've let me down a bucketful, doc. I'm sick of all that talk. I like being Roly. I like being drunk all day and having no responsibilities. I like going about town when and where I like and having a bit of a laugh, acting the goat in the middle of O'Connell Street or Grafton Street. Making people laugh gives me a purpose to my useless life. I'm happy, in my own way, being Roly. I can't see myself ever changing and the best thing you can do is to accept me as I am. Maybe I'll change some day but not right now."

He obviously didn't want to talk about reforming himself so I never mentioned the subject again. One day, when he was resting in the department, I asked him what his favourite drink was.

"You'll never believe this, Doc, but it's tea, Chinese tea with a little lemon. I only drink alcohol to get drunk. I feel so happy and full of good humour when I'm drunk. A lot of the booze I take makes me feel sick. I hate the taste of it, especially whisky, brandy and those ten per cent lagers, rocket fuel I call them but I get them down somehow. If you're referring to what alcoholic drink I really like, then a nice glass of sherry before lunch has to be my choice, Harvey's Bristol Cream, or a drop of port after dinner, preferably a vintage Warners. Nothing but the best for Roly," he added with a grin.

Sometimes when I was off duty, I would bump into him along Grafton Street or Stephen's Green where he used to beg for money. "You get a better class of beggar round Stephen's green," he told me once. "No riff raff there, in fact there's quite a few old College boys like myself."

Sometimes when I came across him downtown, he would be so drunk that he wouldn't recognize me. At other times, he would be charming and jovial.

"Well, hello there, Dr Griffin. How nice to see you on such a pleasant afternoon. You're looking well on such a fine day. How opportune to meet you here." He said to me one day, "You couldn't lend me a tenner, could you Doc? I've met a couple of chaps here," and he pointed at a couple of drunks sprawled on the road at his feet, "I've promised to take them for a spot of luncheon at the Kildare Street Club, but, would you believe it, when I checked my wallet, I found myself completely out of funds."

"I'm sorry, Roly," I told him, "I'm clean out of tenners myself."

"Oh, how unfortunate, Dr Griffin. I suppose I'll have to give the Chateau Lafite '61 and the veal cutlets a bye ball today and settle for a couple of pre-prandial drinks," and he swigged down a large gulp of White Lightning cider from a bottle.

Roly often appeared at the Accident and Emergency Department in a variety of fancy dress. He once turned up dressed as a Frenchman complete with black beret, blue and white hooped pullover, white trousers and a loaf of French bread tucked under his arm. I acted surprised and treated him as complete stranger.

"Sister McNeill," I said, "I think we have someone here all the way from Italy to see us."

That caught Roly napping.

"Italiano, prego, nein, nein, not so you stupeed Britisher. I am a Frenchman. Do you not see zis," and he waved his long French loaf in my face and snort indignantly. "My name is Gaston. 'Ow are you?"

"Your name is Gaston Owareyou? That's an unusual name for a man from Ballybrack."

"Pardon. Vot you mean, Ballybrack. I say I am Gaston and then I tell you 'ow are you, you 'orrible little Englander from a nation of shopkeepers."

"Gaston, you're a bit confused with your countries, Irelander perhaps but hardly Englander. Now what can I do for you?"

"Ver es ze Eiffel Tower s'il vous plait, mein freund. I am looking for it!"

"Hold on a minute, Gaston, mon ami. Are you sure you're French at all. There seems to be a bit of German slipping into your mother tongue."

That stumped Roly for a second or two. He'd obviously taken too much QC sherry before coming into the A and E. It had affected his usual wonderful mimicry. He had a few seconds thought.

"I am from Alsace," he announced. "It is on the French German border. Zat explain vy I speak like a Spanish cow." He was delighted with himself for giving such a clever explanation..

"So, you're looking for the Eiffel Tower in the middle of Dublin are you Gaston?" Sister McNeill interrupted. "Aren't you a bit off course. Perhaps you can give him some directions, Dr Griffin."

"Gaston," I said, "do you see that door there," and I pointed to the exit. "Go through it and keep on walking in a straight line for five hundred and forty three miles and you'll see the Eiffel Tower straight in front of you."

"Danke schon, Herr Doktor. You hev been most kind. May ze fleas from a thousand camels armpits be your inheritance," With that, he clicked his heels and marched out of the department in a goose step with the French loaf slung over his shoulder like a rifle.

On another occasion, Roly came racing into the department dressed as Bluebeard, the pirate, complete with an elasticated false blonde beard that wouldn't fit over his own enormous shaggy one. He was brandishing a cardboard cutlass which he must have stolen from somewhere and he had all the other paraphelanioa one would expect a pirate to have.

"Ahr, Captain," he roared in a mock ferocious voice, "I be looking for a villain who has stolen my chest of gold ducats."

He continued down the lines of patients sitting in the Casualty, waving his cutlass at them and making outrageous threats. Most of the patients laughed at him but some complained about the noise he was making. We had to get him to move on..

I directed him to the door and suggested he contact the Central Bank of Ireland, "I think, Bluebeard, if anyone can find your gold, it will be them"

He was unbelievingly pleased with himself. He thought he had fooled me and the rest of the staff into thinking that he really was a pirate straight off a ship in Dublin Bay.

"I caught you out, the other day," he boasted to me a few days later..

"How did you do that Roly?"

He looked at me out of the side of his eyes. "Did you have someone unusual in here the other day?" he asked.

I knew what was coming next. "We did, Roly. We had an odd looking character who said he was a pirate called Bluebeard. We don't get many pirates about here these days."

"I'll tell you a secret, Doc, but don't tell anyone else. Bluebeard was me."

"What! You're having me on, Roly. The pirate was too fierce to be you. We all thought he was some terrible villain from the Caribbean."

"No, Doc, it was me alright." He was grinning from ear to ear and was as pleased as Punch with himself.

"Well, that was a good one, Roly," was all I could say to him.

One night he turned up dressed as a Chef complete with tall white hat, apron, wooden spoon and a saucepan. On another occasion, he came as a cowboy, calling himself Buffalo William, another time he was a fireman and, one hot summer day, he pushed his way through the entrance attired as a swimmer complete with snorkel, mask and flippers which caused difficulties when he tried to cross the recently washed floor.

He would never tell us where he got all these disguises. We suspected that he stole them from one of the theatres, particularly when he turned up one night dressed as Robin Hood. The Gaiety Theatre was running a pantomime about Robin Hood and his Merry Men at the time. I heard there weren't too many Merry men about the theatre that night when they found their gear missing.

If he was unable to get his hands on a disguise, Roly would improvise.. On several occasions, he presented himself at the nurses' station claiming to be a doctor complete with white coat and a stethoscope. Another time he was a porter wearing one of their green jackets over his own filthy Crombie.

"Hello, I'm the new surgeon sent over from Admin," he introduced himself to me and a group of medical students I was instructing one morning. "I'm to take up my position straight away. Have you any serious cases I can attend to?"

Roly had half stuffed his long, bushy hair beneath a surgical cap and wore a surgical mask that only covered a fraction of his beard. Somehow he had managed to get hold of a surgical gown and this covered his dishevelled clothes. It trailed down to his feet.

"Oh, you're the new doctor," I said as the medical students stared at him in disbelief. "And what is your name if you don't mind me asking."

"My name is Doctor Kildare and I'm from County Kildare. I'm replacing Dr Who."

"Who?"

"Who, Dr Who. Who did you think I said," he retorted.

"So you're Dr Kildare are you? Have you had much experience working in an A and E Department?"

"Oh, I've been around a few corners in my time with this doctoring business," Roly answered. As usual he firmly believed that none of us had recognized him.

Sister McNeill came over to see what was going on.

"Apparently we have a new doctor posted to us, Sister, a Doctor Kildare from County Kildare oddly enough. As it happens, I have quite a bit to do this morning. Maybe we could get the doctor to take the students for a tutorial."

Roly's eyes lit up with delight at having convinced us that he was a doctor and that we were going to entrust him to teach the medical students. The students looked aghast. They didn't know what to say. Sister and I remained poker faced as though we believed Roly really was our new replacement, albeit an extremely badly dressed one. Roly was only too happy to play along with us.

The thought of teaching the students obviously pleased him. He stood up ramrod straight, his arms behind his back and surveyed each student critically. His acting was so good that, for a few minutes, he almost seemed to be a consultant, He certainly looked a lot pleasanter than some of the ones I had had dealings with.

"I'll take these chaps for a ward round, Dr Griffin," he said. "I think I'll teach them a thing or two about distemper, woodworm and brucellosis this morning. There have been quite a few bad cases in the department recently I believe."

As he turned to lead the students off, he noticed a puddle of blood in the middle of the floor. A patient had come in with a badly lacerated leg and the blood hadn't been cleared up. Roly took one look at the blood and began to fall gracefully towards the floor. He couldn't stand the sight of blood. I rushed forward to catch him.

"Are you alright, Roly?" I asked. "You've gone very pale."

As he fainted, Roly pointed weakly at the pool of blood. "Blood m'lud," was all he said.

That was his last appearance as a doctor.

The affect this charade had on the students was interesting. A couple thought it was all a bit of a joke although they weren't too sure that I hadn't set them up, so to speak

The others seemed to think that I was suffering the same mental aberrations as Roly. In fact, I had taken the opportunity to give them a lesson that I felt I had lacked in my own education and that was to weigh up the situation and act accordingly. It didn't matter that Roly was an alcoholic. He was a person and had to be treated. Lecturing him or pushing him to one side wouldn't have helped the situation. It was more important for Roly to think that we understood him and were there to help him. A sense of humour in such situations can achieve so much more than criticism.

What became known as the Roly classic was the time he appeared in the department as a policeman. He came striding in one afternoon dressed as a Garda, wearing a pair of size fourteen boots that were far too large for him. His uniform was oversized as well but he had rolled the sleeves and trouser legs so that it more or less fitted him. He marched up to me and saluted smartly.

"Sergeant Brannigan of the fraud squad," he announced, "reporting for duty, sah."

"Ah, Sergeant Brannigan," I said. "You must be new to the district. I haven't seen you around here before."

"Oh, I've been about alright, doc, undercover stuff, you know," he said tapping the side of his nose.

"007 type work then Sergeant?"

"You've got the picture, doc. Say no more, Sir, if you don't mind. Walls have ears," and he pursed his lips and looked furtively round the department. When he seemed satisfied that no-one was listening, he went on. "Doctor, I believe there have been one or two cases of bogus policemen presenting themselves to this department as bone fide peelers. I have been ordered by my superiors to track down these unscrupulous rogues and give them their comeuppance. Have you seen any suspicious characters about the place recently?"

"Let me see, Sergeant. That's a hard question. We often get a lot of suspicious characters causing a bit of concern but no more than usual in the past week or two. There is a man who comes in here from time to time who has been causing me some concern. I suspect he may be an undercover agent like yourself though I'm by no means sure. His name is Roly."

Roly straightened up with a jerk He didn't speak for a second or two as he stood there and composed himself.

"Roly, Roly, yes, the name is familiar. I know this man quite well, doctor. He's actually a very decent bloke if I might be permitted to say so, sah," and he leapt to attention and saluted me. "However I have been keeping him under surveillance and I must say that I've never found anything suspicious about him. I might add that to my mind, Roly is a model citizen."

"Roly, a model citizen," I said, "now that is an interesting concept but I'm not entirely convinced myself. I have a funny feeling that Roly might be a double agent."

"A double agent is he? He sounds like he could be a right rogue. I'll have to keep an eye on that lad. In the meantime I must continue my beat. Evening all" he said as he lifted his cap to the nurses and left the Department.

One evening a few weeks later, Roly was brought in by ambulance. He was dressed as a clown and had tripped over his enormously long shoes as he was walking down Kildare Street and had fallen in front of a car. He was lucky he hadn't been killed. Both his legs were fractured and he had a bad chest injury. Roly was still conscious. He was very drunk and didn't appreciate how badly he had been injured. The amount of alcohol he had consumed that day seemed to have completely anaesthetised him. I was upset at seeing this basically good natured man brought into the hospital in such a state.

"How are you feeling, Roly?" I asked leaning over him.

Roly looked down at his grotesquely distorted legs and said weakly, "I'm legless, Doc. I've hardly a leg to stand on."

He was admitted to the Intensive Care Unit where he required a chest drain for an enormous puncture of his left lung. His legs were badly broken and needed several operations which were extremely hazardous considering the injury to his chest and the fact that he had to contend with a severe bout of alcohol withdrawal which he developed in the Intensive Care Unit.

However, Roly had an extraordinary strong constitution from living out rough in all sorts of weather for so many years. He made a remarkable recovery. I went to see him several times when he was in the Intensive Care unit but he didn't recognize me.

I went to see him four weeks later when he was transferred to the orthopaedic ward. He was a changed man. He had been shorn of his long hair and beard and scrubbed clean for the first time in years. The fat red cheeks that he had developed from years of drinking too much had gone and been replaced with almost chiselled features. Roly now had a professional appearance and was remarkably serious and self assured. This was the first time I had seen a sober Roly.

"Well, Roly, old man, how are you?" I started in the same manner that I had become used to addressing him in the A. and E. Department.

"I'm sorry," Roly answered in a clipped, formal voice, "have we met?"

That pulled me up short.

"I'm sorry," I said, "I should have introduced myself." I felt uncomfortable with this new Roly. "I am Dr Griffin. I used to deal with you in Casualty when you had a number of medical problems in the past."

"Ah yes, Dr Griffin. I remember you now that you mention it." He nodded his head as if recalling some unpleasant distant memory "I had a number of difficulties over the last few years which I wish to put behind me. I would be grateful if you would honour my wishes."

This Roly was a stranger to me. I felt like slapping him on the back and asking him what had happened to his sense of humour, but he didn't seem like the sort of man you slapped on the back anymore. Instead, I said," Certainly.." I was going to say Roly but somehow the name didn't fit him any more. I looked at the name over his bed – Mr Roland Morgan Barnes.

"Certainly, Mr Morgan Barnes," I said, "I will honour your wishes.

He was discharged from hospital a few weeks later. We never saw him again..

THE EYE NEEDLE

When Harold Wilson was prime minister, he once said that a week in politics can be a long time. A week in an Accident and Emergency Department can seem longer. It can see you through a whole gambit of human emotions and, in this particular department, emotions can be very near the surface from being tired, bored, sad, miserable, irritated, fearful to being happy, exited ecstatic, shocked, panicky back to being tired, bored……….. Infused into this cauldron of emotions is laughter. The most enduring emotion of working in A. and E. departments the world over for me has been excitement, dread and humour.

But some of the accidents with which we have to deal with or BIDs (brought in dead) have filled me with such dread that they still haunt me even to this day. I shudder at the memory of the horrendous sadness that surrounded these traumatic events – the ten year old girl who fell off her bike and fractured her skull, dying a short time afterwards. I had to take her distraught father to the morgue to identify the body. He sobbed uncontrollably as he looked at his dead daughter's frail little body, the head swathed in white bandages, lying on the mortuary slab.

"My little girl," he sobbed. "My little girl. It can't be my little girl. Please tell me it isn't her."

There was the man who brought his twelve year old son in who had been knocked over by a drunken driver. He had been a promising young boxer and his father was so proud of him. His father shook his head in anguish over and over again.

"My life is finished," he wailed. "My life is finished. There is nothing left in my life," and he sobbed and sobbed and sobbed and there was nothing I could do to ease his pain.

There was the big handsome medical student who broke his

neck in a rugby tackle and was paralyzed from the neck down at the age of twenty and the tall, noble looking Iraqi student killed in a car accident on his way to a formal dinner dance lying on the hospital trolley in his black dinner suit as we waited for him to be taken to the morgue – and his tearful father, a diplomat in Washington, coming over the next day to identify him. There was the mother of six who had been accidentally gassed and so many others that brought such sadness to their families and friends. Fortunately these tragedies were not that frequent, otherwise nobody could endure working in A. and E. When they happened, they spread gloom across the department.

The hospital was situated in Dublin not far from the city centre. It was on call for the whole of Dublin every second night, covering an area where almost one million people lived. There was a steady input of patients every night but, particularly from Thursday to Sunday. Thursday was pay day so that was the start of the weekend for many young people. The more they drunk, the more there was for us to do as people fell over or split their heads.

One busy bitterly cold, frosty night, just before Christmas when festivities were in full flow, the ambulance men found a man lying unconscious in Stephens Green. They had been unable to rouse him so they had brought him in to the Accident and Emergency Department. He was identified by a cheque book in his pocket as a Mr Jamieson from North Dublin

Mr Jamieson didn't appear to be drunk and had no sign of obvious injury. The ambulance men had thought he might have been hypothermic. I went over to see him immediately. He was lying very still on the examining couch breathing slowly and regularly. I wondered whatever could be the matter with him. Had he had a brain haemorrhage or an epileptic seizure or was it a diabetic coma?

There was no response when I tried to rouse him. His pulse, temperature and blood pressure were all normal as was his blood sugar level. I couldn't find anything wrong with the man but there was something about this coma that didn't seem right. Why was his pulse so strong and his breathing so regular. It almost seemed that he was asleep or, I wondered, pretending to be asleep. I came to the sudden realization that Mr Jamieson was not unconscious, he was simply pretending to be.

Another urgent case had been brought in and I had to go and deal with that. As I left the examining cubicle, I noticed out of the corner of my eye that Mr Jamieson had moved ever so slightly on the examining couch to take the pressure off his back. "What is he up to." I wondered.

I returned to the cubicle a little while later to examine Mr Jamieson again and I took Sister McNeill, the sister in charge of the department, with me.

Sister McNeill was an excellent A and E sister. She had all the right qualities for the job. She was efficient and well organized.. She was firm but pleasant with her patients and staff alike. She took no nonsense from any of the nurses, medical students or junior doctors who tried to skive off work. She disliked time wasters, particularly drunks or ill mannered people who had nothing wrong with them yet insisted on blocking up the casualty department with trivial complaints. Rudeness of any sort was anathema to her.

Twenty years of working in busy A and E departments in London and Dublin had honed her cynical sense of humour razor sharp. I could see that if Mr Jamieson was not unconscious, he was going to be quickly demoted to her list of forgettable people. He would get the short shift treatment from her.

"You know, James, I think I know this character," she said to me before we went into the cubicle. "I was talking to the A. and E. sister from the Mater hospital about some odd patients they've dealt with over the last year or two and she mentioned a man who is brought in to them every few months pretending to be unconscious. I'm sure his name was Jamieson. Apparently he's brought in by ambulance every five or six months when he knows there'll be a change of staff. He pretends to be unconscious hoping that he'll get a bed for the night. He does it after he's had a row with the wife and is looking for a bit of sympathy. I can tell you, he won't be getting too much sympathy from me, if it is him".

I examined Mr Jamieson again. I must say he was very, very good at pretending to be unconscious, but he wasn't good enough. He let his arms drop like dead weight when I lifted them and didn't try to minimize the impact of them falling. He allowed me to open his eyes without the lids fluttering in a spasm. I was able to examine his pupils with a strong light without him flinching. I slapped his cheeks and rubbed his shin bones, standard ways of trying to rouse an unconscious person. He didn't even grimace.

"Come on, come on, wake up Mr Jamieson," I shouted.

There was not the slightest response.

"What do you think is wrong with Mr Jamieson?" Sister asked.

"To tell you the truth, Sister McNeill," I said slowly as I looked at her, "I'm not sure whether Mr Jamieson is unconscious or dead."

The man gave a shudder of anxiety. Even Sister McNeil gasped with surprise. She recovered quickly when she realized I was not being serious and began to laugh. Being a professional and consummate actress, she rapidly changed her laugh into a fit of coughing. She pulled a handkerchief from her pocket and wiped a tear from her eye. We remained quiet while she tried to control her coughing fit which sounded more like a fit of the giggles to me.

"That's a bad cough you have there, Sister," I said eventually. "You should get yourself a wee cough bottle for it some time."

"Aye, it is, doctor, it is a bad cough alright," she spluttered. "A wee cough bottle is maybe the answer." Neither of us spoke for nearly a minute.

When she had composed herself, Sister commented. "You said you thought, Mr Jamieson might be dead, Dr Griffin."

"Did I Sister?"

"Well, I thought you said you didn't know if he was dead or alive."

"I've never been really good at diagnosing dead people, sister. Its one of those things that happens sometimes, even to doctors, but you see for yourself that his arm drops back like deadweight when

I let it fall. That is a clinical sign and as far as I'm concerned, that means the man is probably dead."

Mr Jamieson made a slight movement of his arm for my benefit. I ignored it.

Sister McNeil took a few deep breaths as she struggled to control herself.

"Dr Griffin," she said, "do you not think this would be a good teaching opportunity for my student nurses. After all they have to learn about life and death. Perhaps with your knowledge about these matters, you could teach them the difference between being dead and not being dead." She said trying hard not to laugh.

"Certainly Sister McNeill, certainly bring those young nurses in. I would only be too pleased to teach them from my limited knowledge. We were all young once and knew little about such matters. It would be a pleasure to educate those young minds on the subtleties of life and death. It is important after all for medical people to be good at diagnosing dead people don't you think."

Sister went out to fetch her three student nurses and while she was gone, Mr Jamieson made a few jerky movements. I pretended not to notice as I made some notes in his chart. When Sister returned, she arranged the nurses around the recumbent figure on the examination couch.

"Dr Griffin has a patient here and he's is not sure whether he is alive or dead, that patient that is not the doctor," she added drily. "He has kindly offered to teach you the difference. What do you think he should do, student nurse Molloy?"

Student nurse Molloy was a big, good hearted, earnest girl from County Cavan. She was completely unaware that someone as senior as the sister could have a sense of humour. She thought seriously before answering. "If, after clinical examination, the doctor is still uncertain as to whether the patient has a heart beat, it could be established by doing an electrocardiograph tracing."

"Well, Dr Griffin, what do you think of Nurse Molloy's suggestion?"

"I appreciate everything student nurse Molloy has said. It was an excellent answer, particularly as she has only been nursing for a few months and I am not in any way dismissing her excellent response but our ECG technician happens to be very busy just at this moment doing several ECG's. I don't think he would appreciate any extra work from me. Anyway I am quite happy with my own clinical judgement. I think this man is definitely dead. I really do think we shouldn't waste any more time for poor Mr Jamieson's sake. Do you not agree, Sister? We'll move him to the morgue. Would you be so kind as to call the porters?"

As I spoke, Mr Jamieson moved his foot quite dramatically. Nurse Molloy gasped. "Doctor, doctor, he moved. Mr Jamieson moved his foot. I saw him move his foot."

"Oh, I don't think so Nurse Molloy. Dead people don't move. It must have been a reflex like the way a dead frog jerks its legs if you give it an electric shock. No, I don't think he moved. Mr Jamieson is definately dead."

"But I'm sure I saw him move," the nurse stammered. "he can't be dead. Dead people don't move."

"Quite right, Nurse Molloy. Dead people don't move, do they Sister?"

"Not usually, doctor," she replied trying to keep her composure.

"You're upset about this aren't you Sister," I said sympathetically.

"Indeed I am, Doctor, very upset."

"Aye, Sister," I said heavily, "life can be hard. There's no getting out of it alive? Would you please call the porters to take Mr Jameison to the Morgue"

"No Doctor, no, please don't," student nurse Molloy pleaded. "I'm sure I saw him move. Please do an ECG before you take him away."

"Well," I said, "I don't know about all this ECG business. There's no point in us doing a lot of fancy tests only to find that the patient is dead at the end of it all is there. I think Mr Jamieson has been dead long enough but, if you insist Nurse Molloy, I'll do a simple test to see if he is still alive. There's only one sure test to find out and it's much quicker than setting up all that cardiac equipment"

"And what's that test, doctor, if you don't mind me asking" Sister said.

"It's an eye test sister."
"An eye test doctor?" Sister was puzzled.
"Yes Sister, an eye test. We'll do a quick eye test."
"But surely you don't expect a dead man to do an eye test."
"No, not that kind of an eye test, not a vision test. It's a little eye test I've invented myself."
"I don't think I'm familiar with that particular eye test myself doctor and I don't think my students are either. Could you please enlighten us?" The student nurses nodded in agreement.
"The test involves what I call the eye needle Sister."
"The eye needle?" Sister McNeil queried.
"Yes, Sister, I need an eye needle to do this test. Could you bring me the largest eye needle you have please. The test is the best of any I have ever seen for detecting dead people."
"What is the eye needle doctor?" student nurse Molloy sounded concerned.
"The eye needle is a modest little invention of my own Nurse Molloy," I explained.
"I have been working on it for some time now and hope to patent it one day. It is a simple little device really. If an examining doctor does not know if the patient is unconscious, dead or trying to have the doctor on, the doctor wakens him with the eye needle. This gentleman has the honour, wittingly or unwittingly, of being my first eye needle volunteer."

There was suddenly a lot of movement as Mr Jamieson shifted about uneasily.

"He's definitely moving now," student nurse Molloy sighed with relief. "He can't be dead. There's no need for your eye test now, doctor."

"We'll test him anyway," I said. "Sister, the eye needle please."

Sister turned to go out of the cubicle and, at the same time, Mr Jamieson sat up with a roar.

"There'll be no eye needle for me you impertinent young pup," he shouted as he leapt off the couch and ran at me with his fists raised. I dodged behind the trolley and pushed it between myself and the angry

Mr Jamieson. He was now very much alive. He swung his fists at me several times before he realized that the nurses' screams had attracted the attention of two hefty porters. He decided to leave, shouting at me as he went. "I'll be back to get you sonny, don't you ever forget it. You'll not be using any of your eye needle inventions on me."

That was the last we saw of Mr Jamieson but I must admit that I kept my eyes open for several weeks in case he did return to carry out his threat.

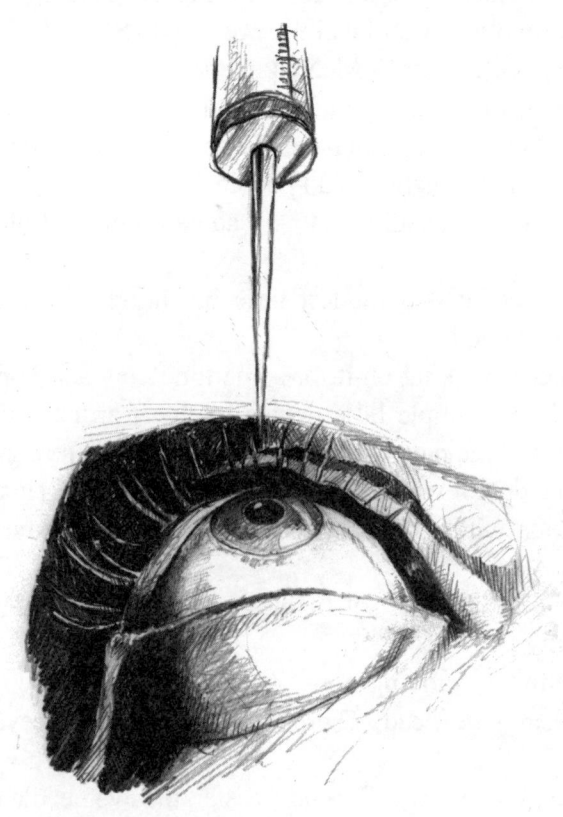

THE FUGITIVE

It was not unusual in an A and E department to be threatened by a patient or a member of his family but, generally, the people who made the threats were pretty harmless and often their behaviour was caused by worry or ignorance. Mr Jamieson had been different. There had been an undermining vindictiveness in his threat and I must admit that I kept a wary eye on the entrance to the department in the following weeks in case he appeared again. But even Mr Jamieson's behaviour paled into insignificance one Saturday evening.

Thursdays and Saturdays were our busiest days in the Accident and Emergency department. Thursday was pay day and many of the workers celebrated by getting tanked up and, by the end of the day, a few of them would have driven their cars into a wall or put their faces in front of somebody's fist. Tough drinking laws had not been introduced then and limiting the amount they drank had not even been considered. Friday was still busy but most people were in recovery phase then preparing for Saturday.

Saturday was our real action packed day, sports injuries during the day, followed by post sport altercations, generally of the fist or boot variety. There was a lull between 7 and 9p.m. before the A&E became seriously congested again. This lasted until five or six the following morning when the last drunk staggered home.

We had a quiet period on this particular Saturday evening. I had just finished stitching someone's head and there was no-one else waiting for attention, when somebody rushed through the doors. He was obviously in a great hurry and sounded agitated. I came out of the cubicle to see what was going on and saw a young man of about twenty standing at the casualty door. He looked panic stricken as he gasped for air. His clothes were torn and covered in mud as though he had been rolling in a dirty road. Blood was pumping out of him from a broken nose and numerous other cuts on his face.

When he saw my white coat, he gave a shout and rushed towards me. Sprinting the length of the casualty department, he frantically grabbed my arm. I had never seen anyone so frightened in my life.

"Doctor, you've got to help me or I'm a dead man," he gasped.

"What's wrong?" I stammered beginning to feel alarmed myself at his obvious terror.

He held tightly on to my arm, oblivious of the blood that was dripping from his face on to the Casualty floor.

"There are some men after me. They'll be here in a minute. They'll kill me if they find me."

"What do you mean, kill you?"

"I mean they'll kill me. They'll kill me dead. You've got to hide me." He stood there trembling like a leaf, his eyes darting from side to side like a trapped animal.

"Get in there," I said, pushing him towards a cubicle. "They'll not find you in there."

He didn't move. He didn't seem capable of movement. "That's no good. That's useless," he stuttered. "They'll find me in a minute. They'll look everywhere. They'll tear this place apart and anybody who gets in their way. You don't know what these men are like. You've got to help me."

He had barely finished speaking when I heard the sound of several men running at speed towards the casualty department. Their footsteps suddenly stopped and I could hear them shuffling outside as if they were uncertain which way to go.

"Go on," I whispered, "get in there" and I half dragged him towards the cubicle, "Just get into that cubicle and don't make a sound. I won't let them in," I tried to sound reassuring. I pulled the curtains across and called two student nurses over and told them to stay with the man and cover him with as many sheets as they could find.

My mind was working overtime. How was I going to stop these men going into that cubicle? Then I hit on a madcap idea. We would have to convince them that there was a woman in the cubicle having a baby. I blurted my idea out to the two young nurses. They looked at me with disbelief and alarm. "If you can think of something better, please tell me now." They stood there shaking their heads. A pregnant woman it had to be.

As I left the cubicle, I bumped into Sister McNeil who was coming on night duty. I grabbed her by the arm and told her to phone the police and get them to come to the hospital immediately. When she saw the anxiety on my face, she turned and ran into the nurses' station and called the local Garda station. Fortunately for us, it was only a few hundred yards down the road.

I had only taken a few steps towards the entrance when five men burst through the door at a run. They slowed down as they came into the bright lights and quietness of the empty department.

They were the most thuggish group of men I'd ever seen. I understood what the man meant when he said that they were going to kill him. Four of them were large and menacing. They stood behind the leader who was no more than five feet tall but incredibly muscular for such a short man. He looked the meanest of them all. Their heads were completely shaven and, above each nasty face, was a bowler hat that looked as if it had been clamped on to their skull bones. They were all dressed the same, short black Crombie coats covered their dirty T shirts and jeans. The legs of their jeans had been cut short to expose massive Doc Marten boots.

Each thug carried an umbrella with a sharpened point. If their faces hadn't looked so vicious, they would have looked comical. Many skinheads had adopted this mode of dress and violence in the early 1970s.

As I stared at them, I felt my courage evaporate. These were dangerous men. I stood there uncertain what to do. How could I have been so stupid to think I could have dealt with men like these on my own. I tried to think of something to say to them but, at that moment, I felt completely out of my depth.

To my relief, Sister McNeil reappeared from her office. She was fearless. The thugs didn't seem to phase her in the slightest. She muttered under her breath, to me as she walked towards them "Would you look at the shape of that short laddie and his trousers. They're at half mast. His cat must have had a sudden death."

I'd no trouble suppressing a laugh when that laddie fixed his wicked eyes on me.

"Good evening, Gentlemen," I said. "What can we do for you?"

"Who are you?" he demanded.

"I'm Dr Griffin, the doctor in charge here. I'm what some people call the casualty officer." I tried to spin out my introduction to gain time. "And this lady is……"

"Shut up," the boss screeched at me. "Where is he?" The boss was obviously a man of limited patience.

"I'm sorry, who are you referring to?"

"You know who I'm talking about, mate. If you don't tell me where he is right now, I'll kick your face in and smash up this dump," and he thrust his face, bulging with veins, into mine. He looked like a mad rottweiler straining at the leash to get at me. "Where is he?" he screamed again. "You better tell me or you'll get what's coming to you."

I really didn't know how to answer him. Sister McNeil came to the rescue. She spoke slowly and calmly. It sounded as though she was taking an elocution class for the benefit of the hoods.

"Please gentlemen please. This is a casualty department, not a lost property department. We deal with injured people here. Has someone been injured?"

For some reason, that seemed to amuse the Skinheads. They all burst out laughing and their laughter sounded as evil as their speech.

"There's someone injured alright you fat cow. We're looking for him and, when we find him, he's going to be a lot more injured. He might even be dead." The boss leered as he looked round at his cronies with an evil grin on his face. "Now you listen to me, you stupid woman if you don't want your teeth kicked down your throat," and he jabbed his face almost into Sister McNeil's. "A man came in here a few minutes ago, We saw him going through that door. We've a little business to finish off with him so just tell me where he's hidden his wee self." He looked round at his followers with a wicked smirk on his face to let them know he'd been funny again.

"I'm sorry, Sir, but I don't know anything about the man you're referring to." Sister McNeil answered as calmly as if she was saying, "no thank you, I don't want another cup of tea" at a garden party.

"Is that so?" screamed Al, the leader of the group. "Well, we'll look for him ourselves and, if we find him, you doc," and he pointed a grubby finger at me, "and you, nurse, will have a doin' over that you won't ever forget."

At a signal from Al, the men scattered, pushing chairs roughly out of the way as they searched for the fugitive. I thought the fugitive's number was up and mine as well. Al was not the sort of person anyone could reason with. He walked over to the cubicle where the man was hiding. He indicated the trail of fresh blood across the floor with the point of his umbrella.

"What's this then, doc, tomato ketchup? I think we might have found ourselves our little friend." He pointed his umbrella at me. "Don't you go too far away, mate. I've a little matter to sort out with you later. I don't like people who tell Al porkies."

As he stalked towards the cubicle, I knew I had to do something to save the man whatever the outcome. I dashed across the floor and stood in front of him. "I'm sorry, Sir, you cannot go in there. There's a woman inside. She's about to have a baby. That's her blood on the floor. The baby could come at any moment.

"Is that so, doc? Well let me tell you something for nothing Mr Smart Alec Doctor, no-one tells me what to do, not now, not ever. Al goes where he likes. I'll look where I like," and he shoved me out of the way with his clenched fist

"That's it," I thought. "The man's had it. There's nothing I can do to stop him 'being killed'.

Al walked across to the cubicle and tore the curtain back. As he went to step inside, one of the nurses screamed.

"Doctor, doctor, come quickly, my baby's coming. I can't stop it. The pain's terrible. Please help me. Help my baby."

This was followed by an awful shriek. It was so realistic, it made me jump. Al let the curtain drop and stepped back. He pushed his umbrella through the curtains and looked cautiously into the cubicle. Both nurses screamed at the same time. I rushed to join them.

"I'm sorry, Sir, I have to ask you to leave. This patient needs my attention. She's in danger of bleeding to death. There's blood everywhere. Come in and look for yourself if you don't believe me."

Al hesitated. He didn't know what to do. Maybe he didn't like the idea of getting blood on his bowler hat.

One of the nurses gave an anguished scream. "Please doctor, hurry. I'm going to die. I know I'm going to die. You must help me and my baby."

Al wasn't sure what to do and I used the situation to slip past him and into the cubicle pulling the curtains behind me. The fugitive was huddled beneath a mound of blood stained sheets. The two student nurses were leaning on him as hard as they could desperately trying to stop him from getting up. He was frantic and was making strange grunting noises as he struggled to get off the couch and make a run for it. He didn't seem to know what he was doing. His arms and legs were flailing everywhere. He did look like a woman in the throes of an agonizing labour. The two nurses were terrified and in danger of becoming hysterical.

I had to do something drastic if I was going to save the man from Al and his cronies. I slapped him hard across his face.

"Calm yourself down missus," I ordered. "Calm yourself right now. What's all that screaming about. I don't want to hear any more of that nonsense. We can't deliver your baby if you're going to carry on like that."

My words seemed to calm him ever so slightly. When he realized that it was me and not Al standing beside him, he settled even more.

"That's better, missus," I said, "much better. Your baby will be alright and so will you as long as you keep calm. Just do as I say. Stay calm That's it. Stay nice and calm. Keep breathing nice and slowly. That's it breathe in and out nice and easy. That's it. Relax, missus. That's good. That's better."

I opened the curtain a little and called to Sister McNeil I asked her to bring some hot water and towels as quickly as possible. I knew that in every film when a baby is about to be delivered, the doctor always calls for hot water and a towel. I thought that Al might have watched some of those films and, by ordering the same, I hoped I would reinforce the idea in his mind that a baby really was about to be born.

It seemed to impress the rest of the gang who had converged round the outside of the cubicle. They stood aside to let Sister through. As she came into the cubicle, I heard the wonderful sound of a siren approaching and, a few seconds later, a police car screeched to a halt outside the Casualty door. Four enormous Gardi tumbled out and rushed inside, followed at a much slower pace by Sergeant Flannigan. When I heard the heavy tread of their boots. I came out of the cubicle. I felt a whole lot safer.

Sergeant Flannigan seemed to take for ever as he casually strolled up the length of the department. When he reached the skinheads, he stood and looked at them for a long time without speaking. They seemed to wilt under his gaze. He walked across until he was facing Al. Sergeant Flannigan was a big man and he towered over him. He stared at him as he crunched the knuckles of his right hand before turning and looking at each of the thugs in turn. As he eyed them, he thumped his right fist into his left hand harder and harder. Nothing was said. There was a silence and a stillness in the big room. None of the skinheads looked at him. They couldn't hold the sergeant's gaze for more than a second.

"Well, well, well," Sergeant Flannigan said at last, "if it isn't Alphonsus, my old friend Alphonsus O'Reilly. Lost our tongue, have we Alphonsus? Usually you're the lad with too many smart things to say, if my memory serves me right. What has all you boys up so late anyway? Been to a birthday party, have you?" He said as he glanced at his watch. "By my reckoning, it must be way past your bedtime. Don't you think so lads."

They didn't answer. They stood there, staring down at the floor and looking increasingly sheepish.

"You know, Alphonsus, it's not healthy for you and your boys to be out in the dark so late at night, is it now?" Sergeant Flannigan continued. "You might get yourselves hurt walking into someone's big, thick fist." He turned and looked at each of them in turn. They all seemed to have lost their courage and exuberance. He ambled slowly over to the biggest of them.

"Well' well' well. Would you look at who we have here? You could almost knock me over with a feather. If it isn't my old friend Benedict, another fly by night boy, if ever I met one. You're another lad who's out far too late for his own good. You'd want to think about running on home now to your Mammy, Benny Boy or she'll have your bottle of milk all drunk,"

Sergeant Flannigan spoke in a soft, gentle voice that had an edge to it which was scarier than any threat.

Alphonse, or Al as he seemed to prefer being called, glanced round at his troops and then at the five large policemen. He'd weighed up the odds and didn't like them. He decided that it was time they left. It was a moment of deep humiliation for him. They made their way hangdoggedly towards the door. As Al passed me, he tried to regain a modicum of pride.

"I'll be back for you, mate," he hissed, "if it's the last thing I ever do."

Sergeant Flanagan and his men escorted the thugs out of the hospital grounds. The sergeant advised them never to come back again anywhere near the A & E Department for 'health and safety' reasons.

"I'm only two minutes away from this place Alphonsus" he said, "and I know you wouldn't want to upset me seeing you here again - would you now?"

During all the furore, the fugitive managed to sneak out of the cubicle and escape through a small window in the mens' toilet. We never saw him again. I often wondered what would have happened if we hadn't tried to deliver that baby.

JAKE

We'd qualified as doctors and if we thought we knew it all then, well, all I can say is that we still had a lot to learn. We knew text book medical practice of by heart but we did not know a lot about people. I really did find myself in a lot of situations that I wasn't too sure how to resolve in those early days. There was always the smart Alec who realised I was recently qualified and would try and wrangle a sick note to excuse him from work or spin me a yarn about his right to some kind of compensation. Experience eventually taught me how to deal with these situations but it wasn't only the patients that puzzled me. Some of the medical staff, particularly the consultants behaved as if they lived in a different world. The occasional junior doctor could have been described as unconventional. Jake was one of the most unconventional doctors I ever met.

He was the only son of the senior partner in a very successful firm of solicitors. His mother had decided his future before he had left his cradle and named him accordingly, Jeremy Alfred Killian Ellison. She was sure that if he joined his father's firm, Jake would finish up as a High Court Judge. To her disbelief, dismay, despair and horror, he decided to become a doctor. To make matters worse he insisted on being called Jake.

"You'll only make a living at that doctoring game, Jeremy," she said," and there'll be all that studying and hard work. You'll never make any real money like you would if you took over Daddy's firm. How many really rich doctors do you know? Oh well, there may be the odd one who has married a wealthy wife or who has an enormous private practice. You would do so much better to work with Daddy."

Jake insisted that he was going to be a doctor. I suppose he felt he had to break out of the mould and by persuading his mother to accept his wishes, he had passed his greatest hurdle in life. Any other problems became mere nuisances and he didn't take any of them seriously. In fact, he didn't seem to take too many things seriously.

Jake was a very light hearted character who liked nothing better than a good laugh. He was one of the wittiest people I ever met and he cheered up everyone with whom he came in contact, both patients and doctors alike, although some of the consultants obviously thought his behaviour was outrageous. I don't think they had ever met anyone like Jake.

He and I became good friends and if we ran into a slack time, we would often wander along to where the other was working and see how he was getting on. I used to meet him at one o'clock each day when the junior hospital doctors and Accident and Emergency staff gathered in the hospital dining room for lunch. The hospital was one of the few that provided good food for its staff. Sirloin steak was on the menu at least once a week. Fresh salmon was a regular item in season as were strawberries and cream and other mouth watering dishes. It was a far cry from other hospitals where I had worked whose height of culinary provision would be greasy chips and sausages and, when they did provide vegetables, they would be boiled to death. The food was so good that most of the junior staff would stay on after a day's work for the evening meal. This was served in the doctor's dining room at 6.30. sharp and staff were rarely late for it.

One evening, when most of the doctors were seated at the table waiting for dinner to be served, Jake was in full flow, entertaining them with his funny stories and mimicry. When he was in one of his high spirited moods, it was impossible to carry on a serious conversation. He was strutting up and down doing an impersonation of a mad General when he noticed Dr Mitchell, the Senior Registrar in Surgery, approaching the table.

Dr Roger Mitchell was a few years older than the rest of us and an extremely talented man. He was tall, broad shouldered, athletic and handsome. To top that, he was a high achiever and had been told that morning that he was going to be made a consultant surgeon at the early age of 31 when a senior surgeon retired at the end of the month.

Roger was one of those dedicated, serious kind of men who also possess a steely determination. Anything he did, he did well. He had boxed at College and become the Intervarsity Boxing Champion. He'd had his nose broken a couple of times but that had only made him more determined to win.

He generally went home for his evening meal but he had delayed leaving that evening after being appointed a consultant. When Roger arrived at the table, Jake jumped to his feet and, standing to attention, saluted him, shouting out like a sergeant major, "Gentlemen, gentlemen, order, order. Please all stand. I present to you Mr Roger Mitchell, our newly appointed consultant surgeon. Hear ye, hear ye."

Jake enthusiastically encouraged us to get to our feet with our glasses of water in our hands and drink to Roger's health. All of us added our good wishes and all would have been well had Jake left it there, but one of Jake's difficulties was that he sometimes didn't know when to stop and he didn't then. Roger was a serious kind of man but he took it all in good humour and went across to take his seat at the table. Jake was right behind him, patting him on the back and telling him he was an outstanding doctor, a good fellow, a man among men.

As Roger went to move his chair, Jake said, "Allow me please, Dr Mitchell, kind sir" and he drew the chair back giving him enough room to sit at the table. As the doctor went to sit down, Jake suddenly pulled the chair back from under him.

Mitchell wasn't expecting such a silly trick and he thundered on to the floor and, as he fell, he tried to grab hold of the table and caught a handful of crisp white table cloth and pulled the whole lot down on top of him, cutlery, crockery, jugs of water, the lot. He was covered by it and the floor glittered with the broken glass.

There was a stunned silence in the room as he tried to extricate himself from the cloth that enshrouded him. He ripped the table cloth from his head and flung it to the ground. His face was white with rage. He didn't say a word as he stared at the quivering Jake who realized only too well that he had made a dreadful blunder. Mitchell stood at his full height and stared angrily at Jake as he clenched and unclenched his fists for several seconds before turning abruptly and marching out of the room.

There was an uneasy silence after he left. Jake looked like a rabbit who had just been pulled out of a magician's hat by a rotweiler. For the first time in his life, Jake did not know what to say. For the next few days, all the good humour and banter of the dining room was very subdued especially when Roger appeared. He was obviously still very displeased.

Jake avoided the dining room and Dr Mitchell in particular. He started bringing in sandwiches and eating them outside in the car park rather than having his meals with us and would peer up and down the corridors to make sure that Roger was not about before he ventured down them. It wasn't easy for two men working in the same hospital and sharing the same facilities to avoid each other but Jake went to extremes to make sure that their paths didn't cross.

We used to meet up in the Common room for a coffee break at eleven o'clock each morning. That was where we exchanged medical views and general chit chat. Jake had always been in the centre of these discussions. He generally had plenty to say but now he started arriving early before anyone else had appeared. He would grab a quick cup of coffee and disappear long before Mitchell arrived. He knew that Mitchell had a busy schedule and always came late for his coffee, if he came at all.

A few days after the chair incident, I went down for my coffee break and found Jake already there. We started to chat but I could see that Jake was very much on edge, keeping his eye on the door, listening to see if Mitchell was in the vicinity. I realized what he was doing and told him that he couldn't spend the rest of his life running in circles trying to keep out of Roger's way. I tried to explain to him that we would have been cross with him too if he'd played the same trick on us.

"All this running and hiding is ridiculous Jake. Why don't you apologize to him the next time you see him and get it over and done with. He's a decent sort of guy. He won't hold it against you."

As I was talking to him. Jake suddenly became very tense. He had heard Mitchell's voice. He was obviously talking to someone and making his way to the Common room for a cup of coffee. Jake and I were the only people in the room at the time.

"Come on Jake," I said, "this is your opportunity. Say you're sorry to Roger."

Jake looked petrified. He stood staring at me with an agonized look on his face then, to my amazement, he made a dash for the enormous Georgian window at the corner of the room. For one dreadful second, I thought he was going to throw himself out of it and pictures of him becoming impaled on the spiked, iron railings three storeys below us flooded through my mind. He flung the window open and scrambled out on to the window sill.

I rushed after him. "What on earth are you doing, Jake?" I asked. "Have you gone completely mad."

"Don't worry yourself, James," he said, "I'm not going to kill myself. I just don't feel I can face Mitchell at the moment. Help me close the window and give it a knock when he's gone."

As he spoke, he pulled the window to and moved to the edge of the sill where he couldn't be seen. At that moment, Mitchell came striding into the room. It was too late for me to open the window again and persuade Jake to change his mind. I stood there not sure what I should do. It was a cold, winter's day. How could I let him stay out on that narrow window sill in such freezing conditions? I spent the whole coffee break in a state of anxiety, thinking that Jake would be getting so cold that he was in danger of losing his balance and falling to the ground. What would I do if he was killed? How could I explain that to his mother?

There was nothing I could do except chat to Roger and prevent him looking towards the window. Fortunately, he was in his usual hurry. He gulped down his coffee and left but, by that time the room was full. Staff and consultants were drinking their coffee and none of them seemed to be in a hurry. How could I open the window in front of them all. I couldn't think of any way I could explain why I had shut Jake outside on such a cold day. By the time I did let him in, he had been out side for forty minutes and he was chilled to the bone.

"I'd never make it as a pigeon or an Eskimo James," he muttered as I let him in. "That height business would do my head in and the cold would kill me."

I wasn't the only one urging him to apologize and, in the end he agreed that he would have to do something but, as usual, he had to do it his own way. A couple of mornings later, we were all in the Common room for our coffee break when Jake suddenly appeared at the door. He was wearing a dark suit and College tie and had his shaggy hair neatly trimmed.

He marched into the room like a sergeant major, slamming the heavy door shut behind him. The noise made us all jump and we turned to see what had caused it. Jake stood to attention just inside the door. He was very tall and as he looked round the room from his great height he took a deep breath and roared, "Gentlemen at ease."

A Spoonful of Medicine

There was a snigger of amusement from the junior staff. Some of the consultants stared crossly at him, a look of disapproval on their faces.

"Who is that chap?" I heard one of the surgeons ask his colleague. "I've no idea" his friend replied, "But he doesn't look as though he's got his wits about him, not the full shilling I should say."

"Seems to be some sort of a military chap," another said, "odd behaviour all the same."

Roger looked away when he saw that it was Jake causing the furore. Jake stood to attention for a few seconds surveying the room imperiously. He seemed quite oblivious to the uproar he had caused. Then he spotted Roger. He jerked his head back, then made a dash for Roger with his two long arms held up in the air. It looked as though he was going to hug him, or strangle him. Instead, he flung himself full length on the floor in front of Roger and, grabbing hold of his ankles, cried out in a loud voice, which sounded louder in the silence of incredulity that filled the room, "Forgive me, Roger. Forgive me for hurting you. I was bad, very bad, very, very bad, the baddest man in the hospital, the baddest man in Dublin' the baddest man in Ireland, the baddest man in Europe, the baddest ...."

His words were drowned as everybody began to laugh except for a few of the straightest and most self righteous consultants. They nearly choked on their Jaffa cakes and then decided they had important business elsewhere.

Roger was half amused and half embarrassed by Jake's behaviour.

"Alright then Jake," he said, "Alright, let's forget about it. Lets leave it be. Please get up like a good man," and he bent down and tried to help Jake to his feet but Jake held on to his ankles like an octopus. When he realized that Roger had forgiven him, he did not know whether to laugh or cry. He scrambled to his feet and threw his arms round him and gave him a great hug.

Hugging was not Roger's thing at all. He detached himself from Jake's grasp and shook his hand keeping him at a distance. Jake was delighted that he had been forgiven and grinned from ear to ear. The happy life of the hospital canteen returned to normal.

You could not be cross with Jake for long. He sometimes seemed like a schoolboy who had never grown up. If I had a slack moment in the Accident and Emergency department, I would pop up to his ward for a cup of tea or to see how he was getting on and he would visit me in the same way. He was full of good spirits and would soon have the nurses and patients laughing. They always enjoyed his sense of humour but, sometimes, he could be a bit too boisterous.

We were chatting in casualty late one evening when a young man staggered in holding a handkerchief to a large wound on his scalp. He was one of those men who, when they are twenty look fourteen and grow a straggly beard as soon as they can to make themselves look older.

"Would you look at that bearded wonder," Jake said as a nurse took the patient to a cubicle, "he looks about twelve."

"It looks as though he needs a few stitches whether he's twelve or twenty," I said as I stood up to go and attend to him. "Come and give me a hand Jake if you've nothing better to do. I'll stitch and you can cut the sutures."

It turned out that Brendan was nineteen. He sat there apathetically as I studied the cut in his head. "You'll need quite a few stitches to pull this wound together Brendan, probably twenty I'd say. That's a very nasty cut you have there. How do you feel about having so many stiches Brendan?"

Brendan shrugged his shoulders. "Yeah, O.K. What about it anyway?" he said in a dull monotone.

His response was like a red rag to a bull as far as Jake was concerned. If there was one thing he couldn't stand, it was apathy. It was a challenge to him. He would be filled with a compulsion to get any apathetic person he met to show some sort of emotional response. It didn't matter whether it was anger, annoyance, fear or laughter as long as they could show some sign of life. Apathetic cool dudes were on the top of his hate list and, at that moment,

Brendan was right at the top of that list.

Jake acted immediately. Clutching hold of my arm and looking at me with mock anxiety, he said in a very loud stage whisper, "Excuse me Dr Griffin but do you feel confident to stitch this man after all the whiskey you drank at tea time?"

"What are you talking about, Jake?" I exclaimed.

"Now don't deny it, Dr Griffin, you know you've the best part of a bottle inside of you and even with your capacity for drink, you know that it makes your hands shake." Jake had a broad grin on his face.

The listless Brendan suddenly became animated. He sat bolt upright and tried to wriggle off the couch. He pushed the green gown and the suturing material to one side.

Jake was enormously pleased with himself.

"Well done, Brendan," he said. "The way you spoke a minute or two ago, I thought you were going unconscious on us. I thought we were losing you. I only wanted to test your response. You seem to have come round O.K. I was only joking about Dr Griffin's drinking. He doesn't drink at all, in fact he's a teetotaller. I'm only trying to calm his nerves down by making him laugh. This is the first time he's ever stitched anyone and he's a bit nervous. He'll be alright once he gets started. It's only your head anyway. Nobody will notice the difference."

Brendan was more alarmed than ever. He jumped off the couch and looked angrily at us both.

"For goodness sake, Jake, give over will you. Stop trying to upset Brendan and annoy me," I said sharply.

I eventually managed to settle Brendan down again and convince him that I wasn't a roaring alcoholic and that I had stitched many dozens of heads. I had only inserted a couple of stitches when Jake spoke again.

"Well Brendan, old son, where did you get that cracker of a cut on your head. Did you walk into a bottle?"

Jake had a habit of calling everyone 'old son,' even if they were old enough to be his grandfather or if they were of a different gender.

"Dunno where I got it," said Brendan noncommittally in a dull monotone. He had relapsed into apathetic mode again.

"You come in here with a gash on your head like the mouth of the Liffey and you don't know how you got it," Jake said scathingly. "Come on old son, you can do better than that. Was it a bottle. You can tell me. I'm a doctor."

"Well, sort of," Brendan mumbled.

"Well, sort of," Jake snorted. "Does that mean a sort of a bottle? What sort of a bottle was it then, old son, a sort of a big bottle?"

"Could've been a big bottle or it could've been a little bottle or it might not have been a bottle at all," Brendan said dully.

Jake looked at me and raised his eyes to heaven.

I put five or six more stitches in Brendan's head as Jake carried on questioning him about what sort of bottle he had been hit with and why he had been hit with any sort of a bottle in the first place. Brendan was not only the least communicative person we had ever met but he was also the dullest and, as far as Jake was concerned, the least entertaining. Jake gradually extracted some information from him by suggesting such outlandish ideas as to the circumstances of his injury . It seemed that Brendan had been standing in a queue at one of the most notorious night clubs in Dublin when a bouncer came over and hit him over the head with something big and sharp.

"It couldn't have been your I.Q., anyway Brendan" Jake said.

Brendan looked at him blankly.

"Look, old son I'll let you into a secret. This tantalizing conversation has given me the mother and father of a migraine, I think I'll need a tranquiliser to settle me down." Jake left the cubicle and wandered off to make himself a cup of coffee, shaking his head in exasperation.

Jake was the sort of person who could make a story about two flies walking up a wall sound interesting. He couldn't understand how someone who had been beaten up couldn't string two words together or make any effort to tell us what had happened. If the same thing had happened to him, he would have had everyone laughing about how he nearly came to a sticky end. He came back into the cubicle 10 mins later carrying a cup of coffee for me just as I was putting in the last few stitches. "James I've put the usual double shot of Vodka into your coffee. Is that enough or will I just leave you the bottle?"

Brendan who had almost fallen asleep suddenly became very alert. He looked at me with alarm.

"I'm an awful liar, Brendan. Griffin here is the biggest alcoholic in all of Dublin. He shouldn't have stitched your head like that. You should see the mess he's made."

With that, he walked out leaving me to try and calm down the suddenly invigorated Brendan. He seemed to have become a completely different personality and I had to get the staff nurse to come across and reassure him. We eventually got him to lie back on the examining couch. I kept on talking as I tried to calm him down and finish the suturing.

"Do you think you'll ever go back to that night club again Brendan?" I asked saying the first thing that came into my head.

"Oh, I'll be back alright. I'll be back there tonight as soon as my head's fixed up to sort out that bouncer," For once, he was talking with some feeling.

"Do you think that's wise after the crack on the head you got Brendan. You wouldn't want another one like it would you?" I was surprised at his foolhardiness.

"There won't be no more cracks on my head doc. It'll be the bouncer that'll have to look out for his."

"How's that?" I began to wonder if Brendan was a boxer or karate expert. Was he going to go back and start a fight?

"Are you a boxer then, Brendan?" I asked.

"No. I don't need none of that stuff to look after myself."

"You're not going back with a knife or a baseball bat or anything like that are you?" I asked beginning to feel uneasy.

"No, I don't need no knife or baseball bat or anything like that to sort out that bouncer."

So you're going back there tonight then Brendan without any sort of weapon at all. I can't see the bouncer being too scared of you."

"Oh, he'll be scared alright. He'll be the scaredest man in Dublin next time he sees me, doc," and he spoke with a feeling that would have astonished Jake. I wondered if the blow to his head had affected him. I was getting concerned about what he was going to do. Even the staff nurse beside me looked worried.

"Why do you think the bouncer will be scared of you?" I asked.

"Oh, he'll not be scared of me. I don't think that for a minute," the enigmatic Brendan replied.

I could see now why Jake had taken a migraine. I felt like grabbing hold of the man, shaking him and making him tell me what he was going on about. To get a story from him was like trying to uproot a tree with long grasping roots.

"What are you talking about Brendan. I can't understand when you say one minute that the bouncer will be scared of you and the next he won't."

"I know he'll be scared, the scaredest man in Dublin."

"Why do you think that?" I was beginning to think that this saga was never going to end.

"I'll tell you why he'll be scared, doc, because I've got nine brothers and they're all over six foot tall. I'm the youngest. I'm the runt of the litter. My brothers don't like nobody to mess with me. Them brothers of mine, they don't scare easily. I'm going home to get them now. They won't be too happy when they see this crack on my skull and I'll tell you something for nothing that bouncer won't be too happy when he sees them either."

I finished the suturing in silence. Jake always referred to Brendan as Brendan the Boring Bearded Bard or the 4Bs. On the rating of one to ten, he gave Brendan ten for being the most boring person he had ever met. It was the start of his own personal marking system. From then on, he would mark people on the same scale but nobody ever matched the ten he gave Brendan. Jake would often poke his head through the curtain when I was dealing with a patient and listen for a minute or two before saying, "Excuse me Dr Griffin, there's a recording of eight on the B4 scale and rising." It could be really disconcerting if I was in the middle of a serious interview with a patient.

Brendan was one of the last patients I stitched in the Accident and Emergency Department. My six month period was almost at an end and I felt I needed to move on and get more experience in children's medicine if I was going to become a general practitioner. I applied for a post as a senior house officer in one of Dublin's children's hospitals. One of the questions I was asked at the interview was whether I spoke Russian. I answered 'Niet.' The only other Russian word I knew was Russian roulette. I thought niet was probably the better answer in the circumstances. Despite my lack of linguistic ability, I got the job.

Jake was also moving on to a new posting, He decided to take up the position of medical officer to an Antarctic Geographic station. He told me when he was leaving that he had heard that the South Pole was a great place to make friends and influence people!

BRATTY

I was assigned to a brilliant, though eccentric, consultant paediatric cardiologist by the name of Dr. Bartholomew Burke when I moved to the Children's Hospital. Everyone knew him as Bratty, not to his face of course. He was exceptionally tall and his most noticeable feature was his nose. He seemed to look down his large nose at everyone and everything with an air of disapproval. He liked to do everything in his own way and at his own pace. He tolerated no criticism and took no advice from any man.

Despite being an ungainly figure, he was remarkably vain. He had his hair cut at the same time and the same place every week. This took precedence over any appointment he might have at the hospital. His pin striped suits were made in Saville Row and his shirts were ordered from a shirt maker in Jermyn Street. His thick, black brogues were hand made by a Dublin cobbler. Bratty always wore a red rose on his lapel and a gold Rolex Oyster watch on his wrist. He was a picture of sartorial elegance and when he walked into the wards it was as if he expected everyone to pay homage to him.

Bratty was a widower. His wife had died after two years of marriage, probably on purpose when she realized the mistake she had made, one of the doctors commented.

He had several obsessive traits, one of them being his collection of Mont Blanc fountain pens. He always had four such pens arranged in the top pocket of his suit, each pen having a different coloured ink, red, green, purple and black in that order. If he found a pen in the wrong, he became petulant. Bratty would select a colour according to his mood. We soon managed to colour code him, red for angry, green for peaceful, purple for upbeat and black for absolutely grim.

His excessive interest in his pens was nothing compared to his obsession with staples and stapling. Staples had to be applied at an angle of forty five degrees to the top left hand corner of the patient's notes and at no more than 1.5 centimetres from the corner of the page to match his precise specifications. The carelessly placed staple was anathema to him. The half stuck staple provoked the immediate use of his black fountain pen

"The correctly applied staple permits the page to be turned over efficiently, effectively and, not least of all, neatly," Batty would announce.

When Batty picked up a patient's notes and found a staple that had not been applied correctly, the whole clinic ground to a halt. A look of irritation would appear on his face and he would hold both his hands in front of him as if he was trying to stop a runaway bus. Angry little noises would erupt from the back of his throat.

"Look at this," he would splutter, "would you look at this. Who is responsible for this?" and he would pick up the notes by the corner and hold them out with a look of disdain on his face.

I worked with him for six months and for the whole of that time, he suspected me of being some kind of staple saboteur.

"Did you do this, Griffin?" he would demand, holding up some incorrectly stapled notes.

"No, Dr Burke, definitely not."

"Well who did it then?" I could see that he didn't believe me.

Nobody owned up.

"Oh, I see," he would say, "it's put itself in has it?. This staple is a self stapler - a very clever stapler?" Then he would fix his eyes on me. "Fix it then, Griffin. Fix this smart, self stapling sheet, NOW."

He had imported a special staple remover from Switzerland and would shove it across the desk towards me. I suppose I should have felt honoured. Nobody was allowed to touch this special piece of equipment with its mock ivory handles except under Bratty's direct supervision. It wouldn't have mattered if a visiting Professor from the Royal Academy of Medicine had been present or if the President of Ireland was on the 'phone. Bratty had his priorities. The staple had to be removed and reapplied correctly before he moved another step.

Soul destroying de-stapling tasks were part of my duties for several months and some of it must have rubbed off on me because, even today, I find myself giving a sharp intake of breath if I come across notes that have been stapled together sloppily.

Another of Bratty's eccentricities was his interest in seating arrangements. He had the chairs we sat on arranged in a straight line in the outpatients department. He would sit behind his desk and the paediatric Registrar and myself would sit beside him but at a measured distance from the desk. Medical students, student nurses and visiting doctors were instructed to sit on our right. We all faced the door. The staff nurse was ordered to stand on his left hand side but away from his desk. When parents entered the room with their child, they faced a forbidding looking man in a pin striped suit behind an enormously heavy desk and a line of doctors, nurses and sundry supernumeraries all staring at them in silence.

We were not permitted to speak to Bratty unless he addressed us. He never asked our opinion about anything. He had enough opinions of his own. Sometimes he would suggest that the registrar and myself go off and have a cup of tea rather than attend his clinic. We never knew if we had offended him or he simply did not want us there.

I was on call one weekend and admitted a six year old boy in the early hours of Monday morning He was listless and had severe diarrhoea, vomiting and a high temperature. I thought he had gastro-enteritis and was severely dehydrated. I put him on a drip and ran in some intravenous fluids and he improved dramatically.

Although it was a Bank holiday the following day, Bratty still expected us to turn up for his usual Monday morning ward round. We were all expected to be there before the great man arrived himself or risk his extreme disapproval. Any latecomers were dismissed and told to come back another day when they had learnt something about manners and punctuality. Even being on duty over the weekend and having no sleep for forty eight hours was not an acceptable excuse to Bratty.

I managed to get to the ward just before he did and was still panting from the exertion of having to race up three flights of stairs to do so.

We followed him through the door in the order that he demanded. He stopped at the first bed, studied the temperature chart in silence and then bellowed, "What's this boy doing in an Infection Isolation ward and taking up a valuable infectious bed?"

"Good morning Dr Burke," I began.

"Don't you good morning me, Dr Griffin. What's this boy doing here?"

"I admitted him at four o'clock this morning," I told him in what I believed to be a firm voice. "He has gastro- enteritis and needed to be isolated and re-hydrated."

"He does not have gastro-enteritis," Bratty shouted. "Who made that diagnosis?"

"I did, Professor," I said quietly. It was impossible to make this man out. How could he decide what was wrong with the patient when he hadn't even looked at him.

"Well, you're wrong, completely wrong," he announced.

"Wrong Professor?"

"Completely and utterly wrong. Get this patient moved to a General medical ward immediately," he told the ward sister.

His abrupt dismissal of my diagnosis and his attitude towards me in front of all the other staff was right over the top.

"But, Dr Burke, Jamie has had diarrhoea and vomiting for three days and a very high temperature."

He turned round and looked at me as if I was a toad that had crawled out from under a rock.

"Exactly, Dr Griffin," he said, "when did you ever see a child with gastro-enteritis who had a very high temperature. It's as rare as hen's teeth. The child has a urinary tract infection."

"A urinary tract infection," I exclaimed with disbelief.

"Yes, a U.T.I., a urinary tract infection."

"But he has no urinary symptoms, Dr Burke. I specifically asked his parents."

"How many times have I to tell you that you cannot treat children like small adults. If they have a urinary tract infection they often have a high temperature with vomiting and diarrhoea. You should know that by now."

When I didn't answer, he turned on me and asked, "Do you not believe me Dr Griffin?"

"I felt certain that Jamie had gastro-enteritis."

"Felt Dr Griffin, felt. That is not good enough for me. You have to be certain and I am certain. That boy has a U.T.I."

My face must have registered my disbelief.

"I am so certain, Dr Griffin, that I am prepared to bet on it without examining the child."

"Bet on it, Dr Burke?"

"Yes bet on it. What did you think I said? I'll bet you five pounds that this boy has a urinary tract infection."

"I'm not a betting man, Dr Burke."

"Everyone's a betting man if the odds are right Dr Griffin. I bet a fiver at ten to one that this child has a U.T.I."

I didn't know what to say. My mind was in a complete quandary. Was I going to get in over my head to even think of betting against the elusive Bratty? Nothing he proposed was ever straightforward. I had to know exactly what he had in mind in case he decided to move the goalposts later.

"Could you explain exactly what you mean when you say you'll bet me at ten to one, Dr Burke?"

"It's quite simple, Dr Griffin I would have thought you'd have understood that. You bet me five pounds. If you win, I'll give you fifty pounds. If I win, you give me five." He took a thick wad of notes out of his back pocket and, peeling off fifty of them, handed them to a pretty nurse with an ingratiating smile. It seemed money for old rope to me. I was so sure of my diagnosis I handed over my five pounds to the nurse. However there was still a lingering doubt in my mind.

"I'm glad to see you're a betting man after all, Dr Griffin," and his chest puffed up with pride. He was so pleased with himself. I would have handed over every penny I possessed at that moment to be right and prove him wrong.

The man was oblivious to my doubts. He had moved up a gear. Snapping his fingers, he ordered a nurse to bring a sample of the boy's urine to him.

"Did you test his urine, Dr Griffin?" he asked with a sly grin.

"No Professor, I took a sample and sent it to the lab to be tested."

"Ah, you didn't test it yourself, mistake number one."

"There is no microscope on the ward for testing the urine," I said.

"Is there not, Griffin. Mistake number two." A smug smile spread across his face. He snapped his fingers again and sent a timid looking medical student off to the microbiology laboratory to fetch a microscope with a warning. "If they try to tell you that you can't have one, tell them that Professor Burke, head of Paediatric Cardiology wants one straight away."

The student returned several minutes later gasping for breath but with a microscope clutched in his arms. As we waited for him to return we stood in a silent line with sister holding the urine sample in front of her.

Dr Burke took the microscope without a word and went to the window, through which the morning sun was streaming.

"Right," he said, half to himself, "let's make some easy money here"

He put a few drops of urine on a slide, talking to himself the whole time. "Now where are the little lads I want to see? Where are those phagocytes and white corpuscles hiding themselves? Where are they hiding? Come on, come on, come out and show yourselves. I know you're there. Show yourselves to Dr Burke and I can collect my money."

He scanned the slide with a ferocious intensity. I had never seen anyone so focused in my life. Perhaps that was the secret of his extraordinary brain power. Then he froze. He had obviously found

what he was looking for. An enormous grin of satisfaction spread across his face. "There are the little lads I've been looking for," and he looked at me triumphantly. "Come on over here, Dr Griffin. Did you kiss that fiver goodbye when you took it out of your pocket. This should teach you a lesson not to bet against the professionals."

His patronizing tone made me cringe. I went over and looked down the microscope.

"Now can you see the little lads I was talking about?"

"No, Professor, I don't see any little lads down there at all." As soon as I spoke, I realized I should have kept quiet.

"Oh come now, Dr Griffin." His voice had a surly edge to it. "You have become the great comic all of a sudden, haven't you. Very humerous altogether." I realized I should have played along with him and acted the clown he thought I was or none of us would be out of the ward before lunch time.

"I can see what you mean now, Professor," I said, trying to do an about turn. "It wasn't gastro-enteritis at all. It was as you said a urinary infection. The slide is full of white cells."

I looked up at him with what I hoped he would think was an admiring grin. He was hugely pleased with himself..

"Now you have learned a little lesson today, Dr Griffin. Haven't you? Leukocytes, phagocytes, white blooded corpuscles, whatever you like to call them, they're the little lads I was looking for. The urine is full of them." He reached out and took the fifty five pounds with a satisfied smirk on his face. He put fifty back in his pocket and stood there holding my five pound note in his hand.

"Now Dr Griffin, you see this pretty nurse here," and he peered at the name tag on her uniform, "Nurse Gillespie," he said. He made a point of never remembering names unless they were likely to be useful to him. She stood there blushing with embarrassment but, as far as Dr Burke was concerned, she was now centre stage..

"I want you to take your five pound back and go down to Brown Thomas's in Grafton Street and buy Nurse Gillespie a nice, new pink, sequinned handbag."

I looked at him in astonishment. Brown Thomas was a ladies' clothes shop and, in those days, gentlemen did not go into ladies' shops of any kind It just wasn't done.

"I'm sorry, Dr Burke, I wouldn't feel comfortable about buying a handbag for any lady. It's not something I've ever done before or wish to do now."

Bratty glared at me and continued waving the five pound note in front of my face. He was obviously getting himself into a very bad temper which would head into a huff and we all knew that his huffs could last for weeks. Then I had an inspiration. "In any case," I said, "it's a Bank Holiday today and the shops are all closed. Brown Thomas will not be open until the morning."

Dr Burke snorted with irritation. He thrust the five pound note in his pocket and continued on his ward round. He did not speak to me again for three weeks. When he did start speaking again, it was quite a shock. He accosted me in the Main Hospital corridor and said. "Dr Griffin, I'll be coming to visit you in Mountjoy Prison."

I wasn't sure I had heard him correctly. "Mountjoy Prison?" I said.

"Yes, Dr Griffin, Mountjoy Prison." There was a look of satisfaction on his face.

"Mountjoy Prison, Dr Burke?" I asked again. I didn't know if he was being serious or if it was another of his bizarre jokes

"Yes Dr Griffin, you heard what I said, Mountjoy Prison. I shall call and see you when you're in there."

"But I don't intend to be in there, Dr Burke," I told him beginning to feel bewildered.

"You'll be in there alright, Dr Griffin. You'll be in there in a few weeks time." He was speaking earnestly and I could see that he meant every word he said. I had no idea what he was talking about but I could see from the look on his face that he was deadly serious. I began to feel worried.

"Why will I be in Mountjoy Prison?" I asked him trying not to let the anxiety I was beginning to feel show in my voice.

"Because the police will take you there, Dr Griffin."

"Why would the police want to take me to Mountjoy Prison, Dr Burke." The conversation was beginning to sound unbelivingly silly but I knew this man well enough to know how crafty he could be. I sensed danger and, as far as I was concerned, I would be on the receiving end.

"Because the Judge will send you there."

"The Judge," I exclaimed.

"Yes, Dr Griffin, the Judge."

"What Judge, Dr Burke?"

"The Judge in the Court House Griffin. Where else would you find a Judge?"

"What Court House are you talking about, Dr Burke?" I was beginning to feel agitated and very perplexed.

"The Court House where you will be going when I report you to the police."

" Report me to the police?" and the astonishment echoed in my voice.

"Yes, when I report you to the police." The level of his voice had not changed and there was still the self satisfied look on his face.

"Yes, Dr Griffin, when I report you to the police ."

"But what have I done that warrants being reported to the police?"

"You'll find out soon enough."

"I can't think of anything that I have done that would warrant that," I said beginning to feel thoroughly alarmed. We had learned all about the problems that we might encounter in medical practice but we had not been taught how to deal with medical specialists like Dr Burke. I was beginning to feel way out of my depth.

Bratty stood there staring down at me as if deciding whether to tell me or not. I looked straight back at him. We must have stayed like that for fully a minute when he suddenly spluttered, "I'll tell you what you did." He was unable to contain his anger any longer. He compressed his lips together and his face went red as the words seemed to be caught somewhere in the region of his epiglottis. "You spoke to a solicitor about one of my patients without my permission. What impudence. Who do you think you are going over my head like that? How dare you?"

"What?" I said feeling none the clearer. Then I realized what he was talking about A few days earlier, a solicitor had contacted me because I was the doctor on duty concerning an inpatient at the hospital. She was in an ethical dilemma concerning the patient and she wanted to know if it would be in the child's best interest if she acted for her. I had answered her honestly, telling her that in my opinion, I didn't think taking up the case would serve either the interests of the child or the parents and would only put them through a lot of anguish and unnecessary expense.. The solicitor seemed to be relieved and Sister told me later that the parents were happy with that decision. The case had been dropped.

"But Dr Burke," I said, "I spoke to the solicitor in what I thought were your best interests. I didn't think you would want to be involved with something so trivial.

"Trivial," he almost exploded and his voice echoed the length and breadth of the corridor, "trivial. This was not trivial. This was a serious case that should not have been dealt with behind my back in such a surreptitious manner." His face had grown even redder The veins on his temple looked as though they were about to burst. He was one angry man..

"I'm sorry Dr Burke. I thought you would have been pleased that I had dealt with that case for you."

"Pleased," he roared, "pleased? Do I look pleased."

"No, Dr Burke, you do not look a bit pleased."

"You overstepped your authority, Dr Griffin. "You will pay for it in the only way that is fitting. Jail is what you deserve and jail is where you will go."

I could see he meant every word he said. I watched him as he continued to march down the corridor, his shoulders hunched. His whole body language displaying his explosive temper.

He never spoke to me again, never spoke a word to me for the three months that I remained working with him. He included Dr Finlay in the sulk for some reason or other and he never spoke to her either, not even to wish her Happy Christmas. He never even asked me to remove another staple.

• • • • • • • •

We were given a talk by Dr. O'Grady one of the consultant paediatricians when we first arrived at the hospital. We were all new boys who had recently finished our houseman's year and fancied ourselves as joining the ranks of this man who was giving us the talk. We were keen and listened intently to every word he said between eyeing up the opposition. I began to feel confident when I saw this batch of other aspiring paediatricians. That was until I met my first patient in the Casualty department.

Dr O'Grady began by emphasizing that dealing with children was not a case of dealing with small adults. We were to remember

A Spoonful of Medicine

that children suffered from diseases not experienced by adults and they also had some diseases that adults suffered but manifested themselves in a different way.

He took vomiting as an example. If an adult vomits, there is usually something wrong with his stomach or intestines but if a child vomits, it could be a sign of a high temperature or an infection, even teething. He then went on to quote what seemed to be an endless list of examples, seeming to take longer with each case that came into his mind.

It was warm in the room and it needed a lot of attention to distinguish one example from another. The new doctor beside me began to nod off and I had to prod him from time to time to keep him awake and prevent his heavy breathing turning into a snore.

"Bear in mind," Dr O'Grady went on, "that when you are treating a child, it is not only the child itself you are treating, it is the parents as well. They are often blaming themselves, rightly or wrongly, generally wrongly, that they are to blame for their child's condition. Sometimes they take their anger and worry out on the doctor – a form of transference of guilt. Some parents may blame the doctor for their child's illness especially if the doctor cannot offer an instant diagnosis or cure. Some parents can become aggressive, even physically aggressive at times. You must not respond to this anger or let yourself feel any anger in such a situation. That would be most unprofessional and doesn't help anyone, least of all the child. You must, in those situations, show empathy and understanding to both the child and his parents.

I had cause to remember his words when I started working in the Children's Casualty Department. An eleven year old boy who was screaming hysterically was rushed into the department by his father. As soon as the child saw the nurses, his screams doubled in volume. His father did absolutely nothing to try and calm his son down. The screams silenced everyone in the area. They obviously thought the noise heralded some life threatening injury. Father and son were shown into a cubicle and I followed them in. The screams intensified when the boy saw me.

A Spoonful of Medicine

Wayne had fallen off his bike and cut his head. I examined the struggling Wayne with some difficulty. His father, a large, overweight, boorish looking man did nothing to soothe his son down or try to control his unbelievable screaming fits. After a brief examination in which I had hardly touched the boy, although he screeched as though I had stuck a red hot poker up his nose, I explained that Wayne needed two stitches in his head wound.

His father immediately became so angry that I thought he was going to hit me.

"What do you mean?" he shouted, almost beside himself with rage. "Are you telling me that you want to put a needle in my son's head? There's no way you're doing that to my son, mate. You're not going to hurt him. You've hurt him enough already pulling his head about like that when you looked at his wound. Nobody's going to hurt my kid no more," he yelled into my face, hunching his shoulders and pulling himself up from his waist. He clenched his fist and looked at me with something akin to hatred.

I was completely taken aback by his attitude. It was on the tip of my tongue to tell him that it wasn't me that had pushed Wayne off his bike but I could see that that wasn't the moment to bring up the subject.

I took a deep breath and noticed out of the corner of my eye that Wayne, despite his great pain, was listening to every word we said very attentively. When he heard that he needed a couple of stitches, he drew in an enormous breath that he held and held until his little face went purple. He suddenly released the air from his lungs in a piercing shriek that echoed down the long corridors of the Casualty department. He screamed and screamed until I thought he was going to burst his lungs. The people in the waiting room must have thought the child was dying a brutal death under what should have been my caring hands. The noise certainly unsettled everyone in the department.

Wayne's father couldn't have cared less who was upset by his son's behaviour. Instead of trying to control him, he rounded on me. "Do you see what you've done to my wee lad now? You've scared the life out of him."

His father's response was a cue for Wayne to lash out with his arms and legs in every direction as he continued to shriek at the top of his voice.

"Dad, don't let them doctors hurt me. I'm not having no stitches, Dad, Nobody's putting a needle into me. Don't let them hurt me, Dad. Don't let them hurt me."

By them, I presumed he meant me. The thought did cross my mind as to whether I really wanted to follow this career and was this going to be the sort of nonsense I would have to put up with for the rest of my working life.

I waited several minutes for Wayne to stop screaming. Between the screaming fits, I managed to say to his father in as firm a voice as I could muster, "It seems that there may be some difficulty getting Wayne to agree to having his head stitched."

"That's your job, mate isn't it? That's what I pay my big taxes for and thats why you get your big, fat salary. Just you make sure you don't hurt my boy Just you be very very careful," There was real menace in his voice.

"I've had about all I can take from this lout and his bolshy son," I thought to myself, "and his talk about the money I am supposed to earn. I doubt if I get a fraction of what he seems to think and, even if I did, it wouldn't be half enough to put up with this sort of behaviour and listen to this sort of cheek.

I took a few deep breaths and said quietly, "I think what we need here, Mr O'Rourke, is a second opinion. Wayne seems to be very upset about his injury. I'll ask Mr Hamilton, the Paediatric Surgical Registrar to come over and have a look at him."

The father glared at me. "About time too, mate," he said. "Why didn't you do that in the first place instead of upsetting my lad? You don't look like someone who knows how to treat kids anyway. You look like someone who doesn't know too much about anything. I don't want no half baked doctor near my son."

I didn't utter a word as I left the cubicle. I just wished I was a very good boxer and in a position to invite Mr O'Rourke outside to sort this out. I phoned Mr Hamilton. He sounded distinctly grumpy to be called out to put a couple of stitches into a child's head in the middle of his extremely busy outpatient clinic. I explained that the father was very upset and the son was extremely uncooperative and that I had only started working in the Children's Department that day. Reluctantly, Mr Hamilton agreed to come over and have a look at Wayne.

Ten minutes later, he breezed into the Casualty department and went over to examine Wayne.

"Well, hello there Wayne," he started, "how are you getting on? I hear you got a bit of a knock on your head," and he leaned over to look at the cut. "I've just come to have a wee look at your and sort it all out."

There was a three second pause as Wayne filled his lungs with air before letting rip a shrill screech that made Mr Hamilton and the nurse beside him jump and instinctively cover their ears with their hands. Wayne's father immediately turned angrily towards the registrar.

"Look what you've done," he started belligerently, "look what you've done to my wee lad, scaring the life out of him with all that talk of yours after keeping us waiting here for so long. What sort of way is that to treat a kid?"

Mr Hamilton took a step back. He was surprised by the ferocity of Wayne's screaming and his father's fierce attack. It took him a second or two to regain his composure.

The Registrar was quite a small man but a very tough and irascible one. He still looked every inch the scrum half he had been when he played rugby for the College of Surgeons. He hadn't been called Hacker Hamilton for nothing. Hacker took no prisoners.

His face flushed with annoyance as he turned towards Wayne's father. He jabbed his finger almost into Mr O'Rourke's face.

"Now you listen to me, mister. I've only just met you but I can see you are one ignorant man if ever I met one. Let me put you straight on one or two points. Firstly, I am not going to take any lip from you or the likes of you. Second, your son's scalp needs

A Spoonful of Medicine

stitching. You can either have it done here or you can clear off and have it done somewhere else. If you don't want me to stitch your son's wound, then my advice to you is to get yourself out of here right now and take your Wayne with you. It's up to you. And another thing while I'm at it, if you decide to stay, I don't want to see your ugly face anywhere near me when I'm stitching him. Do you understand me?"

Mr O'Rourke stood there staring at him. His mouth was working but no sound came from it.

"Now," Mr Hamilton continued, "I'm coming back into this cubicle in two minutes time to stitch Wayne's head. If you're still anywhere in the vicinity when I return, I'm not stitching him and you can take him off wherever you like."

I looked across at the man to see his reaction. If I thought he had been cross with me, it was nothing to the fury on his face after Mr Hamilton's little lecture. He started shuffling his feet as if he was squaring up for a punch up. I wondered which of them would win if it came to blows, Wayne's knuckle headed father or the Hacker. My money was on Hacker.

"You can't talk to me like that," Mr O'Rourke blustered. "Who do you think you are, sonny, telling me what I can do with my son. I'll have my lawyer on to you before you know what's happening. "You'll……..."

"Now you listen to me, mister," Mr Hamilton interrupted angrily. "First of all I'm not sonny to you not now, not ever. If you want to address me, my name is Mr Hamilton. Secondly, go and get your lawyer, get half a dozen lawyers. Bring the whole courthouse with you and, while you're there, get the judge and his Grandmother for all I care. What I told you still stands. Now you make up your mind whether you are staying or going." With that, he turned on his heel and strode out.

I followed him out to the nurses' station. He was pacing up and down seething with rage.

"Did you ever hear the likes of that yob?" he started when he saw me. "The cheek of him telling me my job. I've been training in Paediatrics for more than ten years and that ignoramus thinks he can come in here and tell me what to do. If it's the last thing I do, I'll teach him some manners."

Mr Hamilton was one angry man.

I waited a few minutes until he had started to cool down before I spoke. I couldn't resist the temptation.

"Mr Hamilton," I said, "Dr O'Grady told us several weeks ago during his introduction to Paediatrics that we were to talk nicely to people like Wayne's father. He said that we were to treat them sympathetically and with empathy and understanding. They only seem bad tempered because they're worried about their child."

I thought Hacker was going to explode. It was like showing a red rag to a bull. His face went a shade of purple as he spluttered angrily.

"O'Grady," he burst out, "O'Grady. What does he know about working in casualty?. He hasn't worked here in thirty years. He knows as much about stitching a child as a turnip knows about golf. If he worked with a few Waynes for a day, he'd soon change his mind about empathy and understanding."

I had obviously hit a raw nerve. I decided it would be better if I left the subject of empathy and understanding for the two men to decide between themselves.

Five minutes later, Mr Hamilton went back to see Wayne. His father had gone out to have a smoke, muttering about lawyers and that thug Hamilton. Wayne realized the game was up and, with two nurses comforting him, he gave a couple of muted screams and settled down to have his stitches.

And that was the last we ever saw or heard from Wayne or his father.

THE BANK CLERK

After a year working in the Children's Hospital, I felt I'd had about all I could take of noisy children, hostile parents and all night work. I decided working in psychiatry would be a useful and interesting change.

I applied to several Psychiatric Hospitals around Ireland and got a position as a Senior House Officer in an enormous nine hundred bedded hospital. The hospital had been built in the middle of the 19th century in spacious grounds in the days before any proper treatment for mental illness was available.

Up to the 1940's bed rest, regular meals and plenty of fresh air was the standard therapy for most forms of mental illness. It was known then as the 'Rest Cure.'

Unfortunately this form of treatment didn't work on all patients particularly those suffering from severe depression or psychotic illness. Many of these unfortunate people ended up as long-term patients and spent most of their lives in hospital.

When I was a fourth year medical student in the late 1960s I was assigned to work in a large Psychiatric Hospital for two months under a Consultant Psychiatrist, Dr Prendergast. On the day I arrived at the hospital, Dr Prendergast took a group of students on a tour of the hospital as an introduction to psychiatry.

One of the wards he brought us to was a 'lock-up ward.' It was an enormous ward - the size of a large dormitory and located in a basement floor.

All the walls were painted cream. Light filtered through windows high up on the walls and sometimes when you looked up through these windows you could see people walking past at ground level.

The ward Dr Prendergast took us to was a women's ward. He

told us most of the women had been there for over twenty years. The women were thin and waif-like and they were all dressed in white gowns which combined, with their slow movements, gave them a spectral appearance.

All of the women were lost in a world of their own. The ward was virtually silent as the patients seldom spoke.

Dr Prendergast explained that most of the patients were suffering from chronic schizophrenia which they had developed many years previously.

'You see that unfortunate lady over there,' he said as he indicated an elderly woman who was sitting on a chair rocking herself gently back and forth. 'That's Marie Dougan. Marie came into this hospital in 1908 -over sixty years ago. That's hard to believe, isn't it?'

'She has been here since then. She was admitted when she was eighteen years old with acute severe schizophrenia. In those days there was no treatment for her condition. As she had a tendency to try to escape from the hospital if she got the chance, she was put into this lock-up ward, initially for her own safety.'

'By the time she had settled down enough not to try to escape every time she had the opportunity, she had been here ten years. The staff tried to move her to a more open ward but she refused to leave and has remained here ever since. She rarely moves from that chair and just sits there all day rocking herself to and fro. She'll never leave here now until she dies. She wouldn't even want to. She is completely institutionalised and is unfortunately completely incapable of independent existence.'

Myself and the other medical students expressed shock at hearing about these patients spending most of their lives in hospital. Dr Prendergast explained,' 'It might seem very cruel to you and even to myself, in these enlightened days to hear that someone was put into hospital for life, but you have to look at it in context of the times. In the early part of this century there was no treatment for any mental illness and if a person developed a serious mental illness and wasn't admitted to hospital they frequently ended up roaming the roads until they died from exposure or starvation.'

'Anyone then with a serious mental illness, who was put into a hospital, was considered by their family to be fortunate. It took the responsibility and anxiety away from the family and the patient was fed and looked after reasonably well.'

I was astounded by the sight of so many unfortunate women locked up for life, particularly Marie.

'What made Marie become a schizophrenic?' I asked.

'No-one knows exactly what causes schizophrenia and why Marie in particular developed that condition. There are certain individuals who do seem to have a propensity to develop schizophrenia and sometimes if they get a bad enough shock or setback in their lives, that can precipitate an acute attack of schizophrenia.'

He went on to tell us that Marie had been working in a linen factory and was, apparently from the records, a normal young woman. One evening she came home from work and found her widowed mother and younger brother brutally beaten to death. They never found the murderer although Marie was considered a suspect initially.'

'The terrible shock of her mother's and brother's death and then to be suspected of these dreadful crimes, was too much for someone like Marie. The end result was she developed acute schizophrenia.'

'Nowadays if she developed this illness, she would be in hospital for three to six months and given treatment which would almost certainly help her. The aim would be to get her back into the community to lead a reasonably normal life. But there was no treatment at all for schizophrenia when Marie was young and that is unfortunately the way Marie's ended up.'

Professor Prendergast pointed out several other patients with similar conditions. It was the most shocking introduction to any medical speciality I had ever had.

I was to work with Professor Prendergast for the two month period I studied psychiatry. This attachment involved going to out-patient departments, attending ward rounds and admitting new patients to the ward.

One day Professor Prendergast asked me to go and see a patient of his who had been admitted to his ward the previous evening and to take details from him about his condition.

The patient was a twenty two year old man called John. Up to about a month before being admitted to hospital, John had been a sensible young man who had been working as a bank clerk in a small town in County Meath.

About four weeks before his admission to hospital, the usually quiet and ponderous John had become increasingly talkative and animated.

By the time he was admitted to Professor Prendergast's ward, John was talking virtually continuously day and night. He could barely sit still and moved from place to place without resting. His mother described him as having 'the attention span of a gnat.'

For the four days prior to admission John had not been to bed. He had sat up all night singing and encouraging others in a loud voice to join in with him. His family were at the end of their tether.

To make matters worse, John who, up to then, had been a teetotaller and a non-smoker, had taken up both smoking and drinking with a vengeance. He was drinking ten or more pints of Guinness a day and almost chain smoking half Corona cigars to which he had taken a great liking.

To the amazement of everyone in his village, John was down at the village pub as soon as it opened, where he remained until closing time. He explained at length to anyone who would listen, about his grandiose plans for making a pile of money, by opening a new chain of private banks around the world, over which he would have sole ownership.

He said he would use the profits he made from these banks to lead an exotic lifestyle, globetrotting the world. Prior to his illness, John had never had any ambition to go further afield than Dublin and then only to see the All Ireland Gaelic Football Final at Croke Park.

John had left his job in the bank abruptly a week before his admission to, as he put it, 'concentrate on some serious drinking.'

Just prior to leaving the bank he had caused a furore by his colourful and rude language to clients he disliked and by his generosity to those who were in his favour. He had taken to giving the latter an extra fiver or ten pounds if they were making a withdrawal, saying, 'Put that in your pocket now. It's for yourself. Don't say a word about it.'

He was eventually arrested when it was discovered that he had made large withdrawals from the accounts of several wealthy clients that he thought had too much money.

'I need the money more than those lads do,' he said when questioned by the police. 'I've spent all my own money and those rich lads will hardly miss it.'

When they arrested him, the police soon realised John wasn't a typical thief and that he seemed to have some sort of a mental illness. After one night in prison John agreed to go to hospital for treatment, rather than spend another night in the cells though it perplexed him that he needed to go anywhere near a hospital.

'What am I going to hospital for?' He said. 'I've never felt better in me entire life. I have the energy of ten men. I could out-run, out-eat, out-drink and out-smoke any five men from my home town without a bother.'

The morning I went to see him the nurse on the ward told me John had spent most of the previous night, despite heavy sedation, talking or singing in a loud voice and had kept all the other patients awake.

I introduced myself and sat down beside him.

'Well John,' I said. 'How are you?'

'Well enough nearly doc, and how are you yourself?' John replied very enthusiastically with an infectious laugh.

'I'm fine John, thank you for asking. When you say you're well enough John, what exactly do you mean?'

'What do I mean, nearly doc? I'll tell you in plain English, what I mean. Well enough in my way of speaking, means, powerful altogether, stupendous, magnificent, outstanding, splendid, superb and many other big words besides, which I'll tell you as soon as I can think of them.'

'John, I think I get the general idea,' I said. 'You're feeling very well in other words.'

'Very well is it nearly doc!' He snorted. 'Haven't I just told you I feel stupendous, superb…..'

'Fine, fine, that's fine John. I think I get the picture. I have the impression that you are all of those things that you said, and more besides. Could I clear up one thing with you before we continue. I'm a medical student, John. You can call me James.'

'No nearly doc, I'll not call you James. Nearly doc suits you better. Do you know why I call you nearly doc? You are a doc and you're not a doc. So that makes you a nearly doc,' he added with a great grin of appreciation at his own humour.

'If that's what you prefer….'

'How are you yourself anyway nearly doc?' John interrupted. 'You never answered me that. Is your constitution in good order, the internal organs functioning mellifluously, the cerebrum and the cerebellum in fine working tune….'

'I can't complain John. I'm fine, thank you,' I interrupted. Getting John to stop talking was a problem. He was like a babbling brook that went on and on.

'Can't complain nearly doc? Why do you usually complain?' John continued, obviously paying little or no heed to anything I said.

'Now John, if you don't mind, I think it might be better if I ask you a few questions,' I said a little sharply. I'd been with John now almost ten minutes and had learnt absolutely nothing about him except that he talked non-stop. 'I can't take a history or learn anything about your illness if you keep interrupting me every time I speak.'

'What illness are you talking about nearly doc?' He said. 'I've no illness. There's not a thing wrong with me.'

'Well, Dr Prendergast seems to think you mightn't be your

normal self and he's asked me to talk to you so that I can try and find out what....'

'Dr Prendergast doesn't know what he's talking about nearly doc,' John interrupted sharply. 'He's only a half baked Psychiatrist. Them psychiatrist's.....'

'Please John, if you don't mind, could you just answer my questions. You'll be helping me a great deal.'

'All right, all right, nearly doc. I don't mind in the slightest. I'll answer all of your questions to the best of my ability and more. I'll keep the smart comments and the garrulousness to a teensy weensy minimum and quite rightly so, you're probably thinking. Fire away then nearly Doc. Ask me all the hard questions you can and I'll bounce back the answers and.....'

'John,' I almost shouted, trying to get him to listen to me. 'I want to ask you some questions that are relevant to your condition.' I went on rapidly before he could reply, 'I understand you haven't been feeling too well lately. Could you.....?'

John stood up full of indignation, 'Not been feeling too well lately, nearly doc, not feeling too well. What do you mean by that nearly doc? I'm telling you, I've never felt better in me whole life. If I could bottle some of this feeling I have and sell it, I'd be the richest man in Ireland by tomorrow morning and....'

'Right John, please, please sit down for a moment,' I said as he stood, seething with irritation. 'I think I get the picture.' I had to shout to get him to listen to me.

When he settled down after some grumbling, I asked him a few standard questions to see if I could build up a picture of his life and find some clues as to why he was behaving in this unusual way. John side-stepped and distorted every answer to every question I asked.

I continued to question him. I felt none the wiser half an hour later. I'd learnt nothing about his condition. I was getting very frustrated. How was I going to present John's case to Dr Prendergast when I couldn't get him to answer even the most straight forward of questions?

'Look John. You've got to please calm down for a minute or two and just answer the questions I ask as briefly and as succinctly as you can,' I said for the twentieth time. 'Can you please do that for me?'

'The way I feel at the moment, I feel I could do anything. I...' John started off again.

'Right, John.' I had to yell to get him to stop talking. 'We can't continue with this futile line of conversation. I have to get you to tell me a little bit about yourself. Do you think you could do that without interrupting me?'

'Oh I could do that, nearly doc, no bother. Not a bother at all. Why only the......'

'John, please, could you just answer my questions as briefly as you can. Would that be possible? I would like to ask you about your childhood. Do you think you could tell me a little bit about that?'

'Tell you about me childhood, nearly doc. Of course I could. That's an easy one. That was a happy time. The happiest of times. I remember it clearly. I was born at an early age...'

'Yes, I expect so John, most of us were,' I said wearily.

'I was born younger than most though nearly doc and I decided long before I was born that I'd be born at home.'

'I see,' I said, getting more exasperated by the minute. 'And why was that?'

'I wanted to be near me mother,' he replied with a great laugh.

'I've heard that one before John. That's an old one.'

'Ah nearly doc, you've made me disappointed in myself. I'm very very very disappointed.'

'I'm sorry John,' I interrupted. 'But to be honest, I don't think you're the slightest bit disappointed. Could we try to move on, and could you please try to be a little bit more serious, if even for a few moments?'

'I've never been more serious in me entire life nearly doc.'

'That's good John. I'm glad to hear it. Could you just tell me then about your earliest memory?'

'Me earliest memory nearly doc?'

The nearly doc repetition was beginning to really irritate me. I knew if I drew John's attention to it he'd say it even more often. I gritted my teeth. 'Your earliest memory please John.'

'To tell you the truth nearly doc, me earliest memory has to be the day I was born.'

I was about to get up and leave. I felt John was wasting my time and making a fool of me. I told him so and he suddenly went quiet and pleaded with me not to go.

'Don't go nearly doc. I honestly can remember my birth. Every thought in my head at this moment is so vivid and bright - it's like a picture.' He spoke seriously for the first time since I'd started talking to him.

'Could he be serious?' I wondered to myself. 'Or is this another devious ploy to pull my leg?'

'You can't be serious John,' I said a little uncertainly. 'No-one can remember that far back.'

'Ah no, you're wrong there nearly doc. You're wrong. You haven't been doing your homework, you naughty nearly doc. Some of the great mystical Saints are said to have memories from their earliest infancy. Look at the Holy Friar Padre Pio of San Giovanni in Italy for example - one of the holiest men who ever lived. He only died a year or two ago. He once said he clearly remembered details from his earliest infancy.'

'Are you suggesting that you might be a mystical saint?' I said, pleased at catching him out for the first time.

'Do I look like a mystical saint to you?' John asked facetiously.

'Hard to say John, hard to say, but I think we'll just carry on with your childhood memories all the same, if you don't mind.'

'Going back to me birth then, nearly doc?' John asked.

'Well if you insist.'

'Do you want me to describe my feelings on that occasion or my observations?'

'I think we'll settle for your observations John. I can't imagine you having too many feelings then apart from a thick head after your delivery,' I said, exasperatedly.

'Oh you'd be surprised nearly doc....'

'Observations please John,' I interrupted sharply.

'OK nearly Doc, I'll tell you all about me observations. I remember it like it was yesterday. Shortly after I was born I was dried off by a hefty looking nurse who was a bit rough with the towel. I nearly told her to steady on except of course I couldn't speak, being so young. Do you follow me nearly doc?'

I raised my eyes to heaven. It was pointless trying to get John to talk sensibly. He was obviously enjoying himself too much. 'Have you any more pertinent memories than that nurse John?' I asked despairingly.

'I haven't finished with the nurse or the towel yet nearly Doc. It was a green towel I think, if I remember correctly. Green like the green green grass of home,' and he started to hum a few bars of that song.

'Could we please move on from the colour of the towel, and the nurse?' I cut in sharply.

'And why not nearly doc. It is an esoteric subject, that can only be of interest to a selected few. I'm sure you'll agree.' I nodded my head dejectedly.

'After that rough towelling nearly doc, I was feeling a bit edgy and let a roar or two out of me to clear me lungs and the pulmonary system. I felt the better for it and, decided, for the want of something to do, to have a look out of the window. I saw a young lad leaning on a brush in the hospital car park - a youth of twenty I surmised by the look of him and a hospital employee.'

'I knew by his attitude to the brushing that he was a lazy one. He was pretending to brush up a few leaves every now and then. I says to meself there's......

I was no longer listening as John droned on and on. My head was pounding and I would have left long ago only Professor Prendergast insisted I talk to John for at least an hour.

'John has a classical psychiatric condition James,' he'd said. 'If you talk to him for an hour now, you'll never forget him, believe you me. But more importantly, you'll recognise his illness again if ever you encounter it, for the rest of your life.'

I was still trying to figure out with my extremely limited knowledge of psychiatry at the time, what could possibly be wrong with somebody who talked so much.

John was oblivious to my inner turmoil and went on at great length about the young man with the brush. He was starting to describe what he imagined the mans pension plan might be and how if he invested his pension in John's new proposed banks, even at this late stage, how it might get him out of a rut. I suddenly felt I could take no more of this.

'Right John. That's it. I've had enough. I've had all I can take. I never again in my entire life want to hear anything more about that lad with the brush. It is so irrelevant to your condition and of such infinitesimally small interest to anyone that I feel you should stop talking about it right now.'

'Right now nearly doc?" John asked with surprise. "You don't even want me to tell you about my proposed pension plan for him?'

'No, not another word,' I said emphatically.

'Oh.' For the first time John was speechless. It was several seconds before he continued. 'I'll tell you what though nearly doc, an interesting thing.'

'As long as it's not about that man with the brush.'

'No, it's not about him at all. It's about myself.'

'Well go on then John. Try to be brief. I know you might find that difficult.'

'Oh nearly doc, you are the facetious one and me thinking I was only being chatty. Anyway, the day I was born, when I'd finished perambulating in my mind the diversions of the person who cannot be mentioned, I looked across the fields at the golden sun rising over the sea and casting its rays over the blue blue Dublin

Mountains and I said to myself,

John me boy, this is a great day you've been born on. It's a grand day altogether.' John looked at me poker faced. 'What do you think of that memory nearly doc?'

'Prodigious John,' I answered. 'Absolutely prodigious.'

I shook his hand and left.

The following day I presented as much information about John as I could to Dr Prendergast. I explained the difficulty I had extracting any sort of history from him. Dr Prendergast laughed, 'So John tied you up in knots did he James? I expected as much. John has a condition called hypomania. It's an illness which makes the patient think, talk and behave in an exuberant and extravagant manner.' He went on to describe the features of the illness and told us that the treatment for the condition was Lithium to which many patients responded very well.

John did settle down within a few weeks of treatment to his normal quiet self. He was discharged from the hospital and went back to working in the Bank the following Christmas.

Thinking of the way mental patients used to be treated, I couldn't help thinking how lucky he'd been. If John had been born a generation earlier before the depth of mental illness was recognised, and treatment had been discovered he would have probably spent the rest of his life in an institution.

JACK DEMPSEY

If I thought it was hard work extracting a history from John, I found it considerably more difficult getting any information from the first person I encountered when I went to work as a Senior House Officer in psychiatry.

Jack was a huge man of 43 who looked twenty years older. He had a bloated red face and an enormous beer belly that flopped down over his belt, almost to his knees. Jack had been transferred to our psychiatric unit from a medical ward in St James' Hospital. He had been admitted to St James' with alcohol induced liver failure several weeks before. He had been very ill but with treatment his condition settled down slowly, though somewhat precariously.

He was sent to our unit to continue a 'drying out programme'. On his referral letter the medical consultant in charge had written in red capitals, 'THIS MAN'S LIVER IS IN SUCH A POOR STATE THAT HE WILL DIE IF HE EVER DRINKS AGAIN'.

I went to see Jack shortly after he arrived on our ward, I noticed his second name was Dempsey. 'I'm no relation to the boxer, doctor,' he said jocluarly when I greeted him. 'Though in me hey day I'd have floored that boy on any day of the week before he knew what hit him. I called me left jab, Dempsey's donkey kick. There wasn't too many lads about who could take the donkey kick and stay on their own two feet.'

Jack was a likeable man, though somewhat irascible. He was one of those men who always remain a bit of a lad no matter what age they are. Despite his recent six week stay in St James' Hospital, with strict dietary restrictions, he was still a massive nineteen stone.

'How are you feeling today Jack,' I asked.

'The very best, doctor, and feeling a whole lot better since I lost

A Spoonful of Medicine

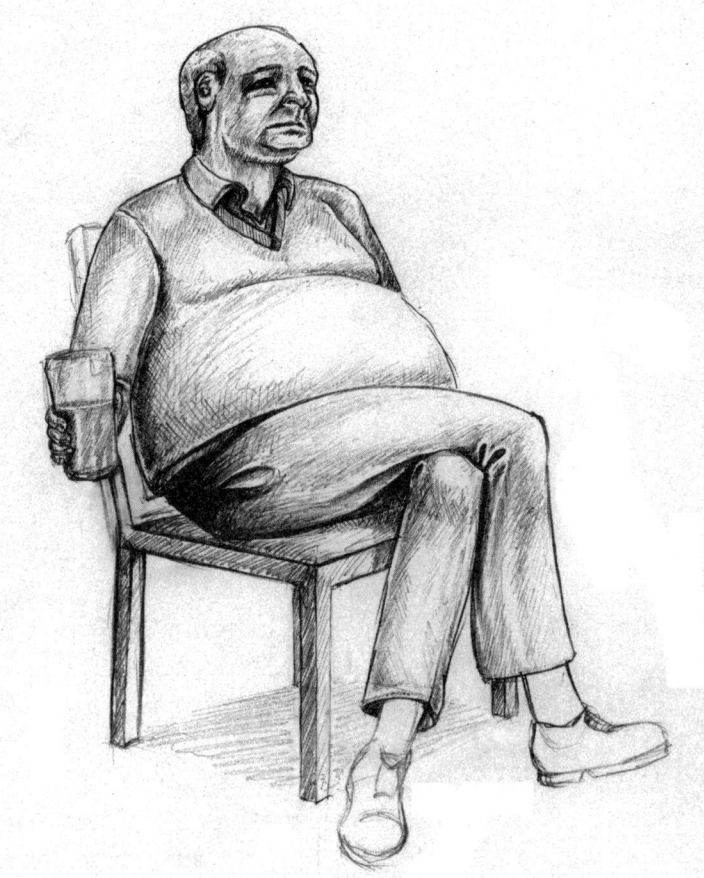

that three stone,' he replied with a grin.

'I see that your referral letter from St James' says you had a bit of trouble with the liver, Jack?' I continued.

'Is that what it says?' he answered, suddenly becoming irritable. 'it's the first time I ever heard of me having any bother with me liver.'

'Is that so Jack?' I said, suprised that Jack had spent six weeks in a Liver Unit and no one had told him he had a liver problem. 'I thought from reading your discharge letter that the doctors in St James' might have explained that to you.'

'Them doctors never explained nothing to me in that hospital,' Jack retorted crossly. 'They never said a word about me liver.'

'Is that so?' I said, concealing my disbelief that he had spent six weeks in hospital and no-one had even spoken to him about his illness.

'In that case I think I'd better let you know what it says in your discharge letter. The doctors from St James' seem to think that you have a problem with your liver and, from what they say here, they are of the opinion that the liver problem might be related to you drinking too much in the past few years.' I added cautiously.

'Me, with liver trouble from drinking?' Jack erupted. He looked at me incredulously, his mouth agape. He looked so cross that, for a moment, I thought he was going to get up and leave. I wondered briefly if I had picked up the wrong discharge letter and given the wrong information to the wrong man.

'No, no, no,' Jack shouted. 'There's no truth in that at all, that's all wrong. They've got that completely and entirely worng. They can't be serious, them St James' doctors. Me, with a liver problem from drinking? It's unbelievable, the stupidity of them doctors - and me six weeks in their ward. You'd think in all that time they'd have found out something about me illness, I've hardly had a single drink in the last twelve months. I'm not a drinker at all. Do you understand me? You young doctors shouldn't believe all the rubbish you read in them hospital letters. There's better men than you has made mistakes from reading too many letters like that.'

I was taken aback by Jack's vehemence and insistence he wasn't a drinker. The merest suggestion that he might have a liver problem brought on by alcohol seemed to enrage him.

'Well, Jack,' I continued warily. 'Doctor Simpson from St James' Hospital seems to be of the opinion that you might have been drinking a bit over the last year or two. It looks to me, from what you say, that you wouldn't agree with his assessment.'

'I wouldn't for one minute agree with that mans assessment of anything, never mind his assessment of me,' Jack said sharply. 'That Dr Simpson doesn't know what he's talking about ...me..drinking.. the cheek of him. Drinking, me eye, is what I say to that. Simpson doesn't know what drinking means.'

Jack looked at me so crossly, I was nearly afraid to continue.

'I understand then from what you're telling me, that you wouldn't accept Dr Simpson's assessment that you're a drinker. I'd be right in saying that, would I?' I repeated, as I wondered what to say to him next. I didn't know what way to approach Jack about his drinking without incurring his wrath - he looked furious at the merest suggestion that he might have an alcohol problem.

'You can take it from me doc, that you'd be dead right when you say that. I don't agree with Simpson's assessment. I have never been heavy on the bottle in me entire life, never mind the past year, or indeed at anytime before,' he answered emphatically.

'So you're telling me then Jack , that you wouldn't have been a drinker at all, at any time? Would I be right in saying that,' I asked guardedly.

'Isn't that what I'm trying to tell you?' Jack almost shouted with exasperation. 'You're getting yourself muddled listening to what that gombeen, Simpson, has written in that letter of his. I'm telling you that I'm not a drinking man and never have been, and I'll tell you something else for nothing, about Simpson and his letter - I wouldn't blow me nose on any letter he ever wrote in case I got whatever disease he has that makes him so crabbed, dreaming up stories like that about me and the drink.'

'Right then Jack, so as far as you're concerned, you would classify as being inaccurate that assessment from the St James' doctors of you being a drinker.... in your own opinion, that is, of course?'

'Completely and entirely and absoloutely inaccurate, doc. A highly inaccurate assessment. The most inaccurate assessment in this hospital, if not in all of Dublin, is what I'd say about that letter. Completely out of order. Me, a drinker?' Jack laughed at the ridiculousness of such a suggestion. He seemed genuinely astonished, that I would even consider he had a drink problem.

'No,no,no,not at all,' Jack went on. 'There's no question of me being a drinker. How many times have I told them that over the past six weeks in St James and they still can't get the message? Sure have I not told you twenty times already that I'm not a drinker. Do you want me to tell you another twenty times again before I can convince you?' He asked, obviously hurt by my lack of belief in him.

'To tell you the truth doc,' he continued with some feeling, 'do you know what one of me neighbours said to me last St Patrick's Day, 'Jack do you know what, you're as near a teetotaller as I've ever met?' Now doc, does that sound like I'm a drinker to you?'

'You've been compared to a teetotaller Jack?' I said. It was my turn to be surprised. I paused for a few moments to gather my thoughts before I continued.

'Could you explain one thing to me then that's still puzzling me a little bit? You've been sent here for a drying out programme and your discharge letter from St James' suggests you were treated for liver failure brought on by drinking and that you'll die if you ever drink again..........'

'Me, dying if I ever drink again?' Jack interrupted crossly. 'That's the greatest load of nonsense I ever heard in me entire life. Haven't I told you already, them St James' doctors don't know what a drinker is. You shouldn't believe one word they say. Haven't I told you that before?'

'So you have Jack, so you have, I don't doubt you said that,' I said, as I tried to appease him. 'I take it then that you wouldn't be too happy to accept the diagnosis from St James' - even after all those blood tests and scans they put you through?.'

'Happy?' he said sarcastically. 'Do I look happy to you? No, not one bit of that diagnosis do I agree with or accept. I wouldn't agree with them doctors at St James' for one moment about anything. You see, that Simpson one, well as far as I'm concerned he's a know nothing. I was wondering many a time when I was in there, if he should be managing me case at all. To tell you the truth, he looks like the sort of a boy who wouldn't recognise a drinker if he met one at a brewery convention. Could he even tell the difference in a pint of Guinness and a bottle of Lucozade?

This interview wasn't going the way I expected at all.

'I see, Jack, I see,' I said, interrupting him as gently as I could. ' I'm sorry, that you're so upset and that I have to be so persistent with these questions, but I need to get things clear in my own mind as well as yours if we're to sort this out in your best interests. Could I clarfiy another point or two with you, if you don't mind? I'll not take too long over it. I know it is very upsetting for you to have to put up with all this but when you say you're not a drinker, what exactly would you say you mean by that in your own words?'

'I mean I hardly touch a drink,' Jack snorted. 'Do you not understand plain simple English?'

'I understand what you're saying alright and what you're telling me and I can see you're not too happy with all these questions I'm asking you, but could I ask you about something that isn't entirely clear to me at this moment .... when you say you hardly touch a drink, is it possible that you could be suggesting that you might take an occasional drink? Would I be right or wrong in saying that?'

Jack looked at me as if I was the stupidest man he'd ever met.

'Of course I take the occasional drink, and why wouldn't I? Is it against the law to take a drink?' he snapped. 'A drink never did anyone any harm, did it? I take a drink now and again to pass meself, so I'll pass meself as good as the next man. Do you not take a drink yourself doc? Is there anything wrong with taking the odd 'ole drink , and, if there is, what has the world come to that a man can't take an occasional drink to pass himself?' Jack answered as he shook his head with disbelief.

'No, no there's nothing wrong with that Jack,' I hastened to agree. 'I have no problem with that at all. Could I ask you to explain to me, that when you say you'd pass yourself Jack, what do you mean by that in your own words?'

'Sure everybody knows what passing yourself means. Do they teach you nothing in them medical colleges nowdays?' Jack said peevishly. 'Passing meself means I hardly touch a drink but if a friend offers me a drink, I'll not pass it by in case I offend him.

Where I come from and I don't know about the rest of ye, we try not to offend a man who offers to buy us a drink. It's called being sociable in my part of the world. I suppose there's something wrong with that as well, by the way you're getting on?'

'There's not a thing wrong with being sociable Jack, not a thing wrong with that at all.... and on that point about being sociable, do you mind if I clarfiy what you mean?' I asked as I tried to placate him. 'You say you hardly touch a drink, yet you were an inpatient in St James Hospital for six weeks with a diagnosis of liver failure..... and I appreciate you don't agree with that assessment for a moment, but would that strike you in any way as being a bit odd?'

'Odd? Odd? It's odd alright,' Jack roared as he rose to his feet, 'it's the oddest thing I ever heard of in me entire life. I'm telling you, I don't think I have a bit of bother with me liver. Them doctors at St James stuck that label on me because they couldn't diagnose what was wrong with me. I'd some quare condition they knew nothing about and couldn't put a name to it. They think they're pulling the wool over me eyes, sticking that diagnosis of liver disease on me but they're not taking me in for one minute . Even if I did have trouble with the liver, it was from a rat bite I got as a boy from swimming in the Canal, and not from drinking. There was a lot of rats about the Canal in them days, biting lads who were swimming in the water. Some of them lads that were bitten got bad johndees (jaundice) from the bites, and went all yella. One or two of them even died from it.'

'Putting aside a rat bite for the moment Jack, which must have happened over 30 years ago, could I just clear up a final point that is still perplexing me? It is important and I hope you'll agree with me, that we get all the facts right and set the record straight for everyone's sake, particularly yours. Would you think that's a fair statement to make?'

'You're dead right. I think it's a fair statement doc. You seem to be getting the picture at long last. I'm all for setting the record straight. I don't want to be put down in no record book that I'm an alco. Go on ahead with your questions - but mind - I told you I hardly know what the taste of drink is,' Jack warned me as he abruptly sat down again, still obviously very irritated by my inability to understand his moderation in the use of alcohol.

'You've mentioned once or twice,' I continued, 'that you hardly touch drink at all but that you'll pass yourself. Isn't that what you just told me?'

'Right as rain doc. I seem to be getting through to you.'

'At the same time Dr Simpson, whether you'd agree with him or not, seems to be of the opinion that you're recovering from liver failure. You'll have to admit that you do have a bit of a stomach on you that looks like it could have held a pint or two of stout in its day, never mind whether the liver failure bit is true or not.'

'Ah well now, doc, that stomach's not worth talking about compared to what it used to be,' Jack said with a sudden touch of pride . 'That stomach could have put away a pint or two in it's day alright - but sure it's nothing like it used to be," Jack continued as he patted his enormous abdomen almost affectionately.

'I'll certainly not argue with you there Jack,' I said. 'And on that point, would that stomach ever have taken on board more than a pint or two of stout in its hey day?

'It would to be sure doc. Wouldn't any dacent man's stomach take on a couple of pints of Guinness, if the occasion was right? Sure isn't it only natural?'

'Certainly Jack. That can be a very natural thing indeed,' I agreed, 'and if you don't mind me pursuing that a little further.... If you had drunk two or three pints of Guinness and had enjoyed them, would it ever have crossed your mind to take another pint or two?'

'Of course it would. Wouldn't it cross your mind? I'm only human like the rest of ye, and humans can make mistakes, at least they used to be allowed to make the odd mistake where I come from.' Jack replied with obvious irritation.'I've seen meself take three or four pints of Guinness in an evening and enjoy them.Why wouldn't any working man take a few pints of Guinness after a hard day's work ? Doesn't he deserve it?'

'Of course a working man deserves a bit of relaxation after a day's work, Jack?' I agreed. 'And if I could just follow on from there, when you say you'd take three or four pints of Guinness on the right occasion, like after a hard days work, would you ever have considered taking more than three or four pints - all things being equal?' I added.

'All things being equal, I probably would have. I'd probably have forced meself. Sure wouldn't you if the craic was mighty and the humor was on you? I'm only doing what thousands of working men in this country and around the world do and that's enjoy meself for a few minutes at the end of a hard days work. Is that a crime?'

'No,no,not at all Jack. Nobody's suggesting for a moment that a pint or two of Guinness after a days work is a crime. That certainly wouldn't be a crime. But say for example it was a Saturday night and you were having great craic and there was music in the background, would you ever have gone on to take more than three or four pints of Guinness?'

'Of course I'd have taken more. Do I look like a monk to you? I'm no abbot in case you haven't noticed. Even monks are allowed to take the odd drink if they're not feeling well and why wouldn't I? I've seen Saturday nights where I've put away three or four pints and maybe even the guts of six or eight pints. Is there anything wrong with that? I suppose you'll be telling me next that's a crime as well. Well, I'll tell you this before you have me labelled a criminal, that where I come from that would only be called wetting your mouth.'

'Wetting your mouth with six or eight pints Jack?' I repeated. Getting information from Jack was beginning to feel as unnerving as extracting a difficult tooth from an angry crocodile.

'Would you have left it at that then Jack - the six or eight pints wetting of the mouth? Would that have been your limit?'

'Ah, what do you mean, me limit?' You can't be serious - me leaving it at that. You don't seem to know too much about drinking either, for all your learning and studying,' Jack retorted. 'Six or eight pints wouldn't be anywhere near me limit. On a good night I'd take ten pints and that might only be me starters.'

'Your starters Jack!' I said, taken aback that Jack had suddenly gone from being a teetotaler to a ten pint a night man in a matter of minutes.

'And what if after your starters, you were still enjoying yourself, would you ever have thought of taking another pint or two?'

'Of course I'd have taken another pint or two and why not? If I was at meself I'd maybe put away another five or six pints,' Jack said, as he rubbed his hands together at the memory of it or maybe in anticipation of doing it again.

'Would you consider that a substantial amount of drink to lower in an evening then Jack- the fifteen or sixteen pints?' I ventured warily.

'What do you mean.. a substantial amount of drink?' Jack retorted sharply. 'You must know nothing about drinking men. I know lads who'd spill fifteen pints on their tie in a night and think nothing of it - never mind drink fifteen pints. They're what I call real drinkers. Fifteen pints would be nothing to them. I consider myself very temperant in the use of drink compared to those lads despite what that Dr Simpson seems to think.'

'Temperant, Jack' I repeated.

'Yes, temperant,' Jack answered crossly. 'Isn't that what I said? Are you not allowed to enjoy yourself any more in this country? What is the world coming to at all, when a man can't have a dacent drink without every nosy parker in the country worrying about it and butting in and trying to stop him? The next thing you know, by the way you doctors are going on, we'll soon need a licence to have a pint of stout.'

'Ah, I don't think there'll be any questions of needing a drinking licence Jack,' I said soothingly, as I tried to calm him down.

'The way the world is now, you never know what'll happen, ' Jack replied cantankerously.'Sure, what do I care about it anyway? The whole world wants to label me as a boozer ... and me hardly touching the stuff.'

I could see Jack was getting completely exasperated by my questions. I decided there wasn't much point pursuing the matter any further.

'I don't think that I'd entirely agree with you Jack that we want to put labels on anybody. I can see you're upset with all my questions and I'll only ask you one final one - if you don't mind - and leave it at that.'

'Ah, sure what do I care about it anyway doc. Nobody seems to believe me when I say I'm not a drinker. Ask away with your questions for all I care and for what it's worth,' Jack replied, sounding very sorry for himself. 'Sure nobody will believe me anyway by the way you are all going on.'

'I'm not saying we don't believe you Jack, I'm only suggesting that some people might consider fifteen or sixteen pints to be a fairly substantial amount of drink..... '

'I don't think fifteen or sixteen pints is a substantial amount of drink or anywhere near a substantial amount of drink.' Jack retorted sharply. 'And what about it anyway, even if it was? You only live once. Are you not allowed to enjoy yourself? You have to make the most of this life, as far as I'm concerned. The next thing I'll hear you're telling me is I should be in jail because I like the odd drink.'

Jack decided that he'd had enough questions and answers from me and stood up to leave. 'You should go away and study a bit about drinkers and drinking young lad, because you seem to know nothing about the subject, which is suprising for someone who is meant to be a medically qualified doctor. I'll tell you this and it's the last word I'll say about it. If I was enjoying meself, fifteen or twenty pints wouldn't even fizz on me. I'd have no problem putting away thiry or forty pints. Now that's the way it is and put that in your pipe and smoke it.'

'Thirty or forty pints!' I gasped. 'That's almost five gallons!'

Jack stared at me crossly for a moment and stalking out, slammed the door after him.

Jack left the hospital after his 'drying out', and went straight to his local pub. He died several months later from liver failure. I found out afterwards that he owned a bar and regularly drank forty pints a day while he served his customers. He drank himself and his business into the ground.

I always remember Jack describing his philosophy for drinking before he died. 'I put each pint to me head twice - once to get the taste of it and the second time to finish it off. It is my belief, and I could be wrong, if you're going to drink, take a dacent drink.'

JUDAS

Jack could be cross, very cross, but he was never violent. Despite having a powerful left jab (the donkey kick) at his disposal if the right situation presented itself, he restricted his fighting to bar room brawls and he made a real impression then. People tended to keep well out of his reach when they saw he'd had a few pints too many on board.

I knew how they felt. I'd been in a few sticky situations myself. Being a doctor in a hospital, there are times when you can't avoid them I think those occasions are becoming a lot more frequent nowadays. I reckon all trainee doctors should have a course in self defence before they ever start their medical training.

There was one occasion when a drug addict I was trying to help suddenly sprung to his feet, smashed a chair against the window of my office and then flung it at me and all because I refused to give him the morphine tablets he demanded. Fortunately I'd had plenty of training on the football field and managed to dodge the chair.

On another occasion, I was examining a fourteen year old boy, checking to see if he had appendicitis. His father had brought him in and was standing beside me. I suddenly realised he was no longer near me and, looking round, I found him standing behind me with his fist raised in the air as if he was about to punch me on the back of my head. I changed my position quickly and carried on examining the boy but I kept my eye on the father and made sure I was nearer the cubicle door than he was. I never understood to this day why he wanted to hit me.

There was another time when I was having a cup of coffee with Sister in her office when a furious looking man charged into the department. He was brandishing a base ball bat and demanding to see a doctor at once. He said he had something to give him and, from the look on his face, I could guess what that was. I stayed where I was and listened as the Staff Nurse dealt with him. She asked him what the problem was and he told her that his mother had died the previous week and it was all the doctor's fault. Sister was used to dealing with people who were trying to come to terms with the loss of a loved one but I doubt if she had come across anyone quite like this man. The man seemed to feel he needed someone to blame for his mother's death and he was blaming 'the doctor', any doctor would do as far as he was concerned I happened to be the doctor on duty. I sank down further into my seat as I silently listened to his angry rantings.

His mother had dropped dead from a massive heart attack in her own home. The ambulance had been called but the paramedics and the cardiac team had been unable to resuscitate her. He couldn't come to terms with her death and was looking for a doctor to give him a good hiding. I huddled down out of his line of vision and stayed very, very still until he left the hospital some ten minutes later under police escort.

When I first met Jack, I was a Senior House Officer in Psychiatry working in a large, Dublin psychiatric hospital. It was part of our training to go out with the Community Psychiatric Nurse (C.P.N.) to visit patients in their homes. It was called, "going on the district." It gave us the chance to see what the patient's family background was like and whether the family was involved with the care of their sick relative.

Some of the patients we visited were loners who refused to attend the hospital out patients department for regular check ups. Left to their own devices, these patients would have deteriorated until they would have been in such a poor mental state that they would have become reclusive without the regular visits from the C.P.N.s

The Community Psychiatric Nurses played an important role in keeping an eye on these unfortunate individuals, making sure that they took their medication and that their condition didn't deteriorate. They also checked that they ate regularly, kept their homes in a reasonable condition and claimed their benefits.

One of the nurses' role was to give long acting injections of major tranquilisers to patients that had long term mental illnesses and who refused to take oral medication.

I went out with Andy Carroll, one of the Community Nurses, every Wednesday afternoon and I would go with him when he was visiting some of his chronically ill patients in Central Dublin.

Andy was a well built, solid looking man in his early forties with a ruddy complexion, bright, twinkling eyes and a lot of Irish charm. He had been working in psychiatry for over twenty years. He was well liked by all his patients.

Andy's best trait was his common sense. The first time I met him, he said, "Most of the work we do, James, is routine. I have been at this job for almost twenty five years and I've had a few bad scares in that time with dangerous or violent patients. Some of it is predictable but some of it comes right out of the blue. It can be easy enough to deal with the violent Psychopath because at least you know what you're up against from the start. It's the old granny with dementia that maybe catches you unawares. You're leaning over the old dear, checking her blood pressure for the hundredth time and suddenly she swings round and butts you in the nose with her head. Perhaps she has a slight chest or urinary infection which has reduced the oxygen supply to her brain and that's been enough to turn her into a bit of a demon."

"Then you get the occasional schizophrenic patient who stops taking his medication and doesn't tell you. When you call in to see him on your monthly visit, you're met by a changed man. He is seething with rage and full of delusions. You might have had the best credit with him on your previous visit but now, all he wants to do is to hurt you. You have to learn a few tricks of the trade in dealing with potentially violent patients, James. There are plenty of violent people about and they're not always mental patients. The first rule is to never turn your back on any of them. Always sit with your back to the door on a hard chair. I know what you're going to ask, why a hard chair? Well, first of all, you're less likely to get fleas and, secondly, it's much easier to get up from a hard chair when you find yourself faced with a charging twenty stone angry man than get yourself out off a soft sofa. Another piece of advice is, never sit too close to a patient or let him approach you if there has ever been a history of violent behaviour. And the last piece of advice I have for you is, when you're visiting a patient in his home, always leave the gate open and don't let the patient lock the door. If they do insist on locking it, get them to show you how to open it. Just make up a story like you're very interested in locks, or that your father was a locksmith, anything as long as you know how to open that door if you ever have to get out of the house in a hurry."

I was to remember this piece of advice a few weeks later in fact, it's been a useful tip that I've remembered throughout my medical career.

A few weeks after I had had that chat with Andy, he phoned me at the hospital to say that he was going to visit an unusual patient that afternoon and he wondered if I would be interested in meeting up with me there. He told me to bring along a couple of needles and syringes and a vial of the depol injection, Modecate that was frequently used for the treatment of schizophrenia in those days.

"I'll meet you at a quarter past two outside this lad's house on Shrewsbury Road," he told me.

"Shrewsbury Road," I exclaimed, "that's one of the wealthiest areas in the city."

"Aye, it is, James," he said, "but mental illness has no respect for money or titles. It can strike anybody, rich or poor. The lad we're going to see is from a very wealthy family. That was part of his problem. He had too much money. He started using drugs and it wasn't long before he tried L.S.D. He took it one night at a party and an hour later, he went ballistic. He didn't come down from Cloud Cuckoo Land for three days and during that time, he went on a spree and wrecked everything around him.

"He's never been the same since. He developed a form of paranoid schizophrenia and religious mania and that was the result of taking that one shot of L.S.D."

"Did he have any symptoms or signs of mental illness before he took the L.S.D.?" I asked.

"None at all. You know yourself that some schizophrenic patients can be withdrawn or loners years before they develop their full blown disease but this lad wasn't like that at all. In fact, he was quite the opposite. He was very outgoing. He was captain of his rugby team at University and, before he grew too tall, he represented Leinster in the 400 m, hurdles. Apparently he was the life and soul of the party and, if you catch him on a good day, you can still some of his old sparkle. And all of that was destroyed because he got involved in drugs.."

I agreed to meet Andy and was just about to put the phone down when he said, "Oh, by the way, James if I'm late getting there, just wait for me. Brian is a man who likes routine. He likes the same people to deal with him the same way and at the same time. He doesn't like his routine upset. He knows me very well but even then I often have to be very wary what I say to him. Most of the time though, he's like a gentle lamb, but a very big gentle lamb."

That afternoon I made my way across town to Shrewsbury Road on my bike. I cycled down the wide leafy avenue with its big, elegant houses set well back from the road. The gardens were luxurious and well shaded with lime and cherry trees. I found the house and waited. There was no sign of Andy. I must have waited for fifteen minutes and I was getting cold. It was a bitterly cold February day with a strong wind blowing and signs of a heavy frost caught along the hedges. I walked up and down and stamped my feet in an effort to keep warm. Another quarter of an hour went by and there was still no sign of Andy.

"Right," I thought. "I've had enough of this. I'll go in, give this lad his injection and then get down to Bewley's for a cup of hot coffee."

I put my bicycle against the hedge and opened the high grill gate closing it carefully behind me and walked up the path. I'd completely forgotten one of the most important rules that Andy had told me. The path took me along a wide, sweeping drive and ended at the front steps of a huge house. I climbed up fourteen steps to the front door and noticed the enormous basement beneath me. I rang the bell. There was no answer. I rang it again. The third time I rang it, I kept my finger on the buzzer for a good ten seconds. I thought I heard a noise like a muffled roar but there was still no answer.. I was about to give up and go back to the hospital when I saw what looked like an enormous shadow moving on the other side of the glazed windows in the huge door.

Before I could move, the door was almost wrenched off its hinges and a massive man in his early thirties stood framed in the doorway. He was seething with anger. The first thing I noticed about him was his size and the second was the clothes he was wearing. He was dressed completely in black. He glared at me with ferocious dark eyes. He had long, jet black hair and a shaggy beard that reached half way down his chest. His appearance did nothing to assure me that he resembled the description that Andy had given him – a very big, gentle lamb. He was big alright but the rest of the description was less than accurate.

He roared at me, "What's your problem, sonny? What are you ringing that door bell like a madman for?. Haven't you seen a door bell before? I'll teach you to recognise a door bell the next time you see one," and he lurched towards me as if he was going to strangle me.

"I'm sorry, Sir, I'm really sorry," I blurted out I hadn't expected this welcome and my mind was working overtime wondering how I should deal with it.

"Andy Carroll asked me to come and see you. He wanted me to give you a message."

By this time the Goliath of a man had me by my throat but he paused when I mentioned Andy's name. I knew I had to keep talking. I said the first thing that came into my head. "Andy asked me to tell you that he'd be calling in to see you shortly, in a few minutes in fact. He didn't want to upset or surprise you by turning up unannounced. He asked me to let you know that he'll be calling."

"Is that so. Hasn't he ever heard of a phone? Why didn't he phone me? Why did he send a crazy guy like you to give me a stupid message like that. What do I need to see him for anyway? I don't need to see him." He paused and looked at me very suspiciously. "I don't want any injections if that's what that Andy boy is thinking about. If he's coming here to give me an injection, if it is I'll wring his neck. Is that why he's coming here?"

I'm normally a very truthful person but I thought this might be the time to tell a white lie.

"Oh no, Brian, nothing like that at all. There's no question of anything like an injection. Andy hasn't got that in his mind at all. He said he was coming to have a chat with you. He invited me along as well. I hope you don't mind. He said you had an interest in religion and, as it happens, I have an interest in religion myself. He thought the three of us could have a chat about religion if you wouldn't mind that is."

Brian eyed me distrustfully

"Alright. We'll wait inside for him. He better come soon or you're in trouble." He took hold of my collar and dragged me into the hallway, shutting the door behind us and locking it in one movement.

Rule number five sprung into my mind straight away. Andy had insisted that if ever I went into a potentially violent patient's home, I was not to allow them to shut the door behind me and certainly not let them lock it.

"Never let them lock you in the house, James." He had said, "however much you might trust them. You must always make sure you have a quick way out and always have your emergency exit planned in your mind."

This situation certainly wasn't working out in accordance with Andy's guide lines. I thought desperately. What would Andy have done? He would have used his common sense and that is what I had to do. I had to see how this door opened before this angry giant of a man lead me down the down into the basement and murdered me. I tried to think of some questions I could ask him but Brian didn't look in the mood for answering anything.

"Come on, come on," he said impatiently, shoving me so violently in the back that he almost sent me sprawling on the floor.

"Could I just ask you one thing, Brian?" I blurted out. "I know it sounds a bit odd to ask but is that a Yale lock you have on your door or is it one of the new Danish locks, you know, the Ruko locking system?"

Brian stared at me without saying anything for a second or two, then he snapped, "What business is it of yours?"

"It's just that I'm very interested in locks. My father's a locksmith and I was wondering what sort of lock this is." I nodded towards the door and took a quick look at it and saw to my relief that it was an ordinary Yale lock and above it there was a brass bolt.

Brian obviously did not share my interest in locks. He grabbed me by the scruff of the neck and shoved me forward. That one movement proved that his strength was formidable.

"Get into that room," he ordered and pointed at a door half way down the hall.

"O.K. Brian," I said. "Andy said he'd be here in ten minutes. I hope he won't keep you waiting too long."

Brian didn't answer. He ushered me into a thickly carpeted room with bay windows that looked out over the massive gardens to the road which suddenly seemed to be a very long way away.

"Sit down," he ordered and pointed to a deep, soft arm-chair in the far corner of the room as far away from the door as it could possibly be.

As I sat down, Brian pulled a tall hard chair across the room and set it down immediately in front of the chair on which I was sitting. There was obviously going to be no discussion about the seating arrangements. He sat on the chair and stared at me. My brain was working overtime thinking how I could calm him down and how was I going to escape. Then I remembered Andy saying that part of Brian's religious delusions was that he was one of the twelve apostles.

"It can be good when he thinks like that," Andy had said, "especially when he thinks he's Simon Peter, the Rock or John the Well

Beloved because he tries to live up to their very high standards but there are times when he thinks that he is Judas Iscariot and that's bad because it makes him very cross and unpredictable."

All this was going through my mind as I looked at him. He was sitting so close to me that I couldn't see anything else. I tried to look at him in a way that wouldn't antagonise him.

Brian sat staring at me for what seemed a lifetime.

"Tell me about religion then," he said at last.

"Religion?" I repeated.

"That's what I said, religion."

"Which particular aspect of religion would you like me to talk about?"

"I was thinking about the Apostles."

"The Apostles?" There was alarm in my voice.

"Yes, the Apostles. Don't you like talking about the apostles?" he snapped.

"Oh yes, Brian, yes I do. I love talking about the Apostles. Talking about the Apostles is one of my favourite things."

"Well then tell me about the Apostles. Which is your favourite?"

"Oh, I like them all. They're all my favourites."

"Are they then? What about Judas Iscariot? Do you like him too?"

"I'm not so sure about Judas. I suppose there's a bit of Judas in all of us if you think about it. Judas was a very complicated man, wasn't he?"

I kept my eyes on his face wondering if I was making him angrier. His face was such an angry mask that it was difficult to know.

"Why, Brian, do you like Judas?"

He let out a roar that sounded like an angry bull. He obviously didn't like that question. His eyes suddenly seemed to bulge out of his head. He opened his mouth wide and I was faced with two rows of large, gleaming teeth.

"What do you mean, I'm like Judas? You blasphemer! What is a blasphemer like you doing in my house? I'll cut out your blaspheming tongue," and, as he shouted, he ran out into the hall.

As soon as he was out of the door, I was out of that soft chair in a second and out of the door right behind him. He made for a door further down the hall and charged into what looked like the kitchen but I didn't pause long enough to find out. I took a sharp turn to the left and made for the front door. I pulled back the brass bolt and tried to turn the key but the snib was in place and it wouldn't turn. I pushed it up with a great effort. At the same time, I heard footsteps coming towards me down the hall. I jerked the door open and took a quick look behind me. Brian couldn't have been more than five steps behind me. His arm was raised above his head and he held an evil looking carving knife in his hand.

I squeezed through the door at the same time as he lunged at me. I pulled the door shut behind me, slamming it in his face and ran. I bounded down the fourteen steps in two leaps and raced down the gravel path. I reached the gate in a matter of seconds. He must have taken the steps in one jump. I could hear his heavy footsteps gaining on me, so much for him being too tall to run fast. I realised as I approached the gate that I wouldn't have time to open it. I was going to have to clear it or be stabbed to death. I cleared it. I didn't know I was capable of making such a jump. It was a lot higher than anything I had ever cleared as a schoolboy high jumper but then, in those days, I had never been so highly motivated. I landed on the other side and I was still running. I pulled my bike out of the hedge and leapt into the saddle and pedalled as if my life depended on it. It probably did. Brian pulled the gate open and ran after me for several yards before throwing the knife after me. I was some thirty yards in front of him by then and it landed harmlessly in the road.

I slowed down at the end of Shrewsbury Road to catch my breath when I spotted Andy chugging along in his old Morris Minor. I flagged him down. He seemed quite shocked by my panic stricken appearance.

"You're not going to see Brian are you?" I blurted out. " Because believe me Andy, it is not a good time to go and see him about anything."

I told him what had happened and he contacted the family. They managed to calm the man's rage down enough for Andy to go and talk to him. It turned out that he had not been taking his medication for over a month and had become increasingly paranoid and angry. In the end, he had to be brought into the psychiatric unit as an involuntary patient. He did settle down after several months and was allowed home on an increased dose of his three weekly injections.

I learned several useful lessons from the experience, one of the most important being to never let myself get into a religious debate with a patient and the second was to never ever close a gate.

OBSESSION

I never forgot Andy's words that mental illness is no respecter of wealth or intelligence and, as I grew more experienced, I realised how true that is. It's not only mental health either. Good health is one thing that money and position cannot buy.

There are many famous people who have suffered from depression or anxiety, two things that can be difficult for the specialist to cure. Abraham Lincoln was so depressed at times that he would be unable to work and would lie on his bed for days.

He coped with his condition by going out and chopping logs We now know that strenuous activity releases endorphins (stress busters). Winston Churchill was debilitated at times by what he called his black dog, a form of depression. Samuel Johnson had the same complaint while the Conservative Prime Minister, Harold McMillan suffered from extreme anxiety, particularly when he had to answer questions in the House of Commons, something he absolutely dreaded. It was said that President Kennedy was so nervous at his swearing in that he had to hide his hands because he couldn't stop them shaking.

When you consider that one woman in eight and one man in twelve will need to be seen by a psychiatrist in their life time, it is not surprising to realise that members of the medical problems can suffer similar problems themselves. After all, they are only human.

When I was a student, learning my trade so to speak, we had a patient who had worked as a doctor on one of the wards in the hospital. He would be admitted on a regular basis and sometimes he would be in for months at a time. He had been the sole consultant Physician in a County Hospital and had had an enormous work load and a lot of responsibility. It was too much for him. He began to take more and more time to get through his work and his ward rounds became longer and longer. He started to examine each patient methodically and repeat full examinations when they weren't necessary as well as taking very long and detailed medical histories of each patient and the patient's family as well. In the end he was spending so much time with each patient that he could only deal with two or three on a ward round and the other twenty seven would be left unattended.

He started going to the hospital in the evenings to try and catch up and often wouldn't leave until after midnight, agitated because he still hadn't finished his ward round. Then he would be back in the ward before many of the patients had woken up.

He hardly slept.

Then, one day, he ran out of the hospital shouting, "There's too much to do and I can't cope with it. I can't stand it any more."

What had gone wrong with Dr Nelson was that he had let his naturally methodic mind takeover his life. He set his standards too high. Everything he did had to be done to perfection. As we live in an imperfect world, perfection is hard to achieve and even harder to maintain. Dr. Nelson could not accept that.

When I came back to the hospital some seven years later as a Senior House Officer in Psychiatry, Dr Nelson was still a frequent visitor as an in patient.

Dr Nelson was a tall, thin, reserved man with a professional demeanor. Even on the ward, he dressed immaculately, a pin striped suit, white shirt, black shoes and a conservative tie. His finger nails were always perfectly manicured. He spoke in a slow measured voice but was reluctant to speak to any of the junior staff, probably through embarrassment, although he was always polite

I got to know him because he was on my ward. He spent most of the day reading and going for walks round the hospital grounds, always taking the same route. He once told me that if ever I found myself in a job that was too stressful, I should only stick it for a short while and then leave it before it destroyed me.

"Look what stress did to me," he said, "work became an obsession. It made me a broken man. I've been in and out of this place for ten years now and all I can think about is my work. I know I'll never go back to it and I wouldn't want to but I can't stop these obsessional thoughts about work going through my mind all the time."

Dr Nelson never fully got over his problem but he did eventually leave the hospital never to return. He had always been musical and was a wonderful pianist. He found he had a gift for teaching music and that was what he did.

I have met many people suffering from mental disorders of one kind or another. There's a line that most people avoid crossing and that is when habit becomes obsessional. I suppose I was introduced to this when I first left home and went to Dublin as a medical student. Dublin then was a different city to the multicultural, pluralistic city of today. Most students stayed in digs and I was no exception.

I lodged in a large terraced house in Fitzwilliam Square. Mrs Benson, the landlady was a widow woman with two grown sons. She was a tall, hefty woman who always wore a floral apron and had curlers in her hair which she hid under a scarf. I never saw her without curlers in her hair. She'd probably been good looking when she was younger but years of grumbling had changed that. She ruled the house and her motley group of lodgers with a rod of iron.

I shared a room with Oliver a trainee accountant. Five nights a week, Oliver would be fast asleep in his bed by ten o'clock while I studied by the light of a lamp in the corner of the room. Friday and Saturday nights were a different matter altogether. They were the nights that Oliver hit the town. He would stagger back around six o'clock in the morning and fall onto his bed, fully clothed with his boots on and lie in a stupor until five o'clock in the afternoon when he would get ready for a repeat performance. In the meantime I would have gone down to the library for two or three hours study, had a game of football and arrived back to the digs just as Oliver was beginning to surface.

I tried to make him understand that these drinking sessions were not doing him much good and he was missing out on so many things in life. He agreed with everything I said.

"I know you're talking sense, James" he would say "but to tell you the truth". I've never felt worse in my entire life. Do you know what, I think I'll have to go for the cure? I'll maybe cut back on the drink next week" he would say.

"But will you, Oliver," I would say. "You said that last week."

"I mean it this week. I guarantee you that I'll be in bed by nine o'clock tonight."

"Do you mean tonight or tomorrow morning Oliver?"

The conversation was repeated weekly.

Among the other lodgers there was Thomas, the bank clerk and Pat the engineer from Galway, John the joiner and Paddy the labourer who had spent most of his life in London as a tunneller on the underground but I think the most interesting lodger was Edward who was an assistant in a solicitor's office.

Edward was in his late 50s and must have been a handsome man in his day. He had closely cropped white hair, an Errol Flynn moustache and always wore a three piece tweed suit, white shirt and an academic looking tie. Mrs Benson loved Edward but the feeling was not reciprocated.. She always gave him the best cooked sausage and the choicest piece of bacon. Edward took it all graciously. Two or three times a week, after our evening meal of potatoes, cabbage and either bacon or fish followed by custard, jelly and tea, Edward would light his pipe and ask Pat, the engineer, in his most formal tone, "Pat, are you at liberty tonight to take a trip down to Dornans Lounge Bar for a drop of stout?"

"I think I am, Mr Lordan. I think a pint of stout after that lovely meal would go down extra well."

The two of them would go off showing a great deal of courtesy to each other. I would hear them coming up the steps to the front door around midnight as I was getting ready for bed. They would be singing a bar or two of 'Take me Home again, Kathleen' or a few lines from 'Galway Bay'. It was years after that I realised how lonely these two men must have been. What they both needed was a good wife - like Mrs Benson but a good deal less ferocious.

One evening when we were having our meal, Mrs Benson was really cross with me for telling the other lodgers how we dissected the cadavers in the Anatomy room.

Edward interrupted and said, "Mrs Benson, if you don't mind, I would like to her James out. I was once a medical student myself at University College, Galway."

"Were you Mr Lordan?" Her voice was full of admiration.

"I was indeed, Mrs Benson, but due to some unfortunate misunderstandings, I was asked to leave."

He then explained how his social life had got in the way of his studies and he hadn't obtained the required marks to pass his anatomy exam. His professor had called him in and told him that he would have to repeat his examination in September. But Edward told the Professor he thought he had been cheated out of a mark that would have allowed him to pass.

"Whether you feel cheated or not, Lordan" the professor had told him, "you will have to resit the exam in September or leave the College."

I told him I wasn't going to repeat any exam. I was a bit brash in those days. I had never repeated an examination in my life. When I had taken my school leaving certificate, I was the first in all of Ireland. Repeating exams was not for me. I got up and shook his hand and left the room and the College."

"Did you regret that decision, Mr Lordan?" I asked. I was a bit brash in those days myself.

He looked at me without speaking for a long time and his eyes clouded over. Then he got up abruptly and left the room. He never mentioned the subject again.

I left the digs several weeks later. Mrs Benson seemed to resent the fact that I was studying to be a doctor and her favourite hadn't become one. She started playing silly tricks that made it difficult for me to study such as coming in and winding up the clock when I was working in the dining room or appearing with a hoover or a cloth to clean the windows when I was trying to study in my room. I kept waiting for her to disturb me and, in the end, I simply couldn't concentrate on my studies.

I moved into a bed and breakfast establishment on Lower Mount Street. Despite that it was a much friendlier and lively house than Mrs Bensons. I spent all my spare time studying. I kept thinking of Mr Lordan and his failure to pass his exams. I was determined that wasn't going to happen to me. Fortunately most of the other lodgers in Lower Mount Street were serious students from Spain, France and America. They were studying too so it made it easier for me.

I took great care to organise the way I studied and spent three or four hours at my books each evening. As the exams approached I would top that up to nine or ten hours. I found the hardest of all the medical examinations I ever did was Pathology because of the amount of knowledge I needed to know. I was completely exhausted at the end of my Pathology exams and went home to Northern Ireland to recuperate. The morning after I arrived home, I went for a walk. I must have gone a mile when I was overtaken by fatigue and knew I couldn't go any further, so I climbed into a field and rested against some hay bales. I soon fell asleep. At that time there was a sectarian murderer on the loose in the area. The next thing I remembered was being roughly shaken awake by two policemen who had been told to go and investigate a suspicious looking body lying in a hay field.

There are long hours of study required if medical students are to pass their exams. It is no wonder that some of them find the work load too stressful and leave the course. I remember the long summer evenings when I was longing to be outside but I had to spend the time studying and memorising tracts of information, the 12 cranial nerves for example, olfactory, optic, occulomotor, trochlear, trigeminal, abducens, facial, vestibulocochlear, glossopharnygeal, vagus, accessory and hypoglossal. Once the student has absorbed that list of names, he then has to learn the route each nerve takes to get to its destination and what structures it passes under, over or near, how each nerve functions and how they malfunction.

When I worked as a Senior House Officer in Psychiatry, I didn't find it difficult to relate to the problems one of the medical students was experiencing. We were doing a ward round when my consultant asked me to see a third year student who needed to be seen as an emergency. He had become extremely distressed and was suicidal.

I saw David that afternoon. He was a quiet, polite young man. He was twenty-one although he looked young enough to be a schoolboy. He was reluctant to talk about himself but after a few prompts from me, he began to open up. All his worries and fears suddenly spilt out of him like a torrent.

He said that he had been studying hard and doing well until a few weeks earlier. It was the beginning of March when he had passed his Pharmacology exam with second class honours. He had only narrowly missed first class honours. He immediately started preparing himself for the two exams that he was to take in June, Pathology and Microbiology.

Pathology is regarded by most medical students as the hardest of all the University exams and once you get it out of the way, you are almost guaranteed that you will become a doctor, as long as you continue to study.

David had been feeling tired after completing Pharmacology. He took three days off, then got down to his studies again. He found it hard to concentrate so soon after finishing his last exam and soon realised that he had probably spent too much time in the Christmas term studying Pharmacology when he should have been doing the groundwork for Pathology. He realised he had set himself an uphill task and that worried him. His confidence was set back further when the Professor of Pathology set the class a small test to see how they were progressing. There were eighty students in the class and thirty-two of them failed. David was one of them.

The Professor was livid

"This is the worst result I have ever seen in all my time in this University," he stormed. "Thirty- two students failing is a disgrace. What sort of reflection is that on my teaching? I can see some smiley faces round this lecture hall. Well those people might think it's a joke but I don't. And for you jokers who find it funny, let me tell you one thing. I have found out over the years that the students who fail this so called little test of mine usually fail the main exam in the summer. Those jokers can forget their summer holidays when they realise they have to do their repeats in September. So think about that before you have your laugh."

That speech wiped the smiles off a lot of faces, including David's. He had never failed an exam in his life and he knew that he had only failed this test because he had spent too much time studying Pharmacology.

He began to panic. He studied longer and longer hours, not going to bed until the early hours of the morning. He drank countless cups of coffee to help him keep awake so that he could study more and that meant he couldn't sleep when he did go to bed.

"It was terrible," he said. "I would eventually fall asleep about six o'clock in the morning and the alarm would go at eight and I would have to face another day of drudgery. I gave up playing sport or going out with my friends. I just studied all the time. The more I studied, the less I seemed to know. I thought that the books I was using did not give me enough information so I bought more text books and that meant there was a lot more reading for me to do. The more I did, the more it seemed I had to do. I started feeling anxious and couldn't think of anything except the Pathology exam. I didn't even have time to eat and I lost my appetite. The weight fell off me. I couldn't sleep and I was going round in a daze. I started to feel depressed. I couldn't concentrate and that made me feel more depressed. I became very irritable and paranoid and started to blame myself for many of the things that had gone wrong in the world. I know that sounds crazy but I couldn't help myself. I realised that myself but I couldn't do anything about it. I began to suspect that there was something seriously wrong with me if I was having thoughts like that.

"I began to think that I was bad and dirty and that if anyone came in touch with me, they would become bad and dirty like me.

I felt I was spreading infection wherever I went and whenever I touched anything so I started to wash myself several times a day. If I touched anything remotely dirty, I would think I was dirty and contaminated and that I was going to infect other people and may be the cause of their death. I began to wash my hands. Then I thought to wash them once was not enough so I would wash them a second time, then a third, perhaps five, six or even seven times. I ended up spending a lot of time washing myself. I knew it wasn't normal to feel like that and to behave in that way but I couldn't stop myself.

"I've never had a day's sickness in my life and these feelings were completely alien to me and alarming too. I was afraid that my friends would begin to notice how often I was washing my hands and the other odd things that I was doing but I couldn't stop it.

"I began to notice objects lying on the road or footpath that I felt shouldn't have been there. If I saw a piece of glass on the road, I would worry about it. I would think that if I didn't pick it up, a car would run over it and get a puncture and maybe crash and kill some innocent pedestrians and it would all be my fault because I hadn't picked up that piece of glass. It was the same with nails and stones. I just had to pick them all up. My life was a complete misery. I couldn't go anywhere without picking up objects which I thought could be potential dangers. It took me ages to walk down a road or get anywhere and I was terrified that one of my friends would see what I was doing and think I was mad."

"If I did leave a nail or piece of glass on the road, I would worry about it for the rest of the day and the worry would often keep me awake at night. I couldn't think about anything else. I would have to go back and find it and pick it up, no matter how long it took or how late at night it was. My life became a living hell."

"One day, I was walking home with some friends. I had been studying in the library but I hadn't been able to concentrate at all. All I could think about was a piece of glass I hadn't picked up that I'd seen lying in the road earlier in the day. I couldn't chat with my friends. All I could think about was that piece of glass. I used to be the joker in the group but that all seemed a long time ago.

"Then I became aware of a strong smell of gas blowing across the road. I was immediately panic stricken."

"Do any of you lads smell gas?" I asked.

"One of my friends paused for a second and sniffed. "Yes, what about it?" he said.

The other two shrugged their shoulders and walked on.

"But that whiff of gas had a dreadful impact on me. What if there was a gas leak and it seeped out and killed all those people living in the houses nearby. It would be my fault if I didn't alert them to the danger. I made a lame excuse to get away from my friends. I realised they were looking at me oddly but I didn't care. I had to do something. I had to sort out this horrible gas problem or I would have gone mad."

"I rushed back to the place where I had smelt the gas but I couldn't smell anything unusual. I paced up and down for the next hour trying to track down the smell of gas.. I knew I was behaving like a madman but I also knew that if I didn't track it down, there wouldn't be any sleep for me that night."

"I couldn't find a gas leak but that didn't pacify me. Maybe there had been a leak and I'd missed it. It would still mean it would be my fault if someone died. In the end I phoned the local police, but what a job that was. I had no change for the phone and had to walk a mile to find a shop that was still open. Then I had to find the name of the street and that meant walking back another mile. I was totally mentally and physically exhausted and at the end of my tether by the time I phoned. I realised that the policeman who answered the phone thought I was either a mad man or a hoaxer but I didn't care. As long as I could pass over the responsibility of the gas leak to someone else I would be satisfied.

"Look, Mister," I finally said to the policeman, "there's a gas leakage at the upper end of Heytsbury Street so sort it out if you want," and I slammed the phone down. I knew by his voice that he thought I was crazy."

"I was able to relax after that because it wasn't my responsibility any more but I still slept very badly that night and couldn't do any study the next day. I knew I needed help and I went to see the College Doctor. He arranged this urgent appointment and that's what has brought me here."

David drew in a deep breath and sat back in his chair. He seemed relieved that he had got that off his chest.

"What's wrong with me?" he asked. "Am I going mad? Is there anything you can do to help me? Am I going to have to give up doing medicine? I can't do that. It's all I've ever wanted to do as far back as I can remember."

He looked at me with intense anxiety as he waited for my answer.

"You have a mental condition known as Obsessive Compulsive Disorder David. It's sometimes called an obsessional illness. It's a very painful condition and leaves the patient very distressed and I know you can appreciate that if anyone can. No, you will never go mad. I can guarantee you that, though patients with your condition certainly feel that they are going to, but it never happens. I know you haven't studied Psychiatry yet but you will, I know you will and you'll understand the condition much better then." I was looking directly at him as I spoke and he smiled. He smiled for the first time and I could see the relief in his eyes.

"You'll be a fourth year student next year David, and you'll study Psychiatry then. You'll find that so called madness in medical terminology is usually reserved for conditions called psychosis, something completely different from the illness you have. If you want to get better, you'll have to do some things you may not particularly like doing such as going on an antidepressant tablet to settle your depression and anxiety. You'll also have to take something to help you sleep. I need to get you to speak to the consultant in charge, Dr Prendergast, to decide what is the best treatment for you."

Dr Prendergast wanted to admit David into the ward straight away but David was absolutely insistent that he was not going to be admitted to hospital. He was going back to College.

A Spoonful of Medicine

"I'm going to get through medicine and become a doctor if it kills me and I'm going to pass Pathology if it's the last thing I do. So please give me whatever treatment I need and I'll take it and go home."

I saw David a week later and his obsessions were as bad as ever though the anti-depressants had taken the sharp edge off them. He was sleeping a little better and somehow managing to go to College and study though not very effectively.

I saw him every week after that and he made unusually good progress for someone with OCD. It is a condition that usually takes years to recover from as in the case of Dr Nelson. David was the most determined person I ever met in my life and he was determined to conquer his illness.

Two weeks before the Pathology exam, he told me that he was going home to County Cork for twelve days and he was going to study twelve hours a day. He said he was going to contain his obsessional thoughts for that period, put them on hold, he said, and pass that exam, come hell or high water.

That is exactly what he did. He returned to College the night before the exam and studied in the train all the way from Cork. He went straight to his lodgings and studied until four the next morning. He got up at six o'clock and studied until nine when he raced on his bike to the Examination Hall and arrived just in time for the half past nine start. He read the questions and knew that he could answer four of them and could make a tentative effort at the fifth..

David scraped a pass in Pathology. He cancelled his plans to do his third year Medical Elective in France and spent the summer fishing and sleeping at home.

I never saw him as a patient again although I did bump into him some fifteen years later at a medical meeting in Dublin. He was pleased to see me and thanked me for helping him through the worst experience of his life. He said that it had taken him five years to recover from that illness. That was only through your sheer determination, I thought to myself.

He said that his illness had taught him more than any medical education could ever have. I understood what he meant. He was one of the kindest and most understanding of men I ever met.